GLASGOW'S 100 BEST RESTAURANTS

GLASGOW'S 100 BEST RESTAURANTS

© Glasgowist Ltd. All rights reserved.
First edition printed in 2019 in the UK.

ISBN 978-1-5272-4954-7

Published by Glasgowist in partnership with heraldscotland.com

Written by Paul Trainer

Contributors: Rosalind Erskine, David Kirkwood
Photography: Clair Irwin, Sonya Walos, Naomi Vance
for Atomic10, Newsquest, Glasgow Life, Cate Devine

Design: Oli Breidfjord at Bright Signals
Layout: Ian Corcoran

Thanks to: David Craik, Susan Sullivan and David Ward

Printed by: J. Thomson Colour Printers in Glasgow

Email: hello@glasgowist.com

GLASGOW'S 100 BEST RESTAURANTS

By Paul Trainer

This is your restaurant roadmap for 2020. Accept an invitation to explore the city, roam unfamiliar streets and discover a new favourite food place. It's also a chance to become reacquainted with some of the culinary highlights that define our local hospitality scene. Each has its own charms and individual reasons to be celebrated. They collectively share one thing: You won't find them anywhere else. We've brought together local food stories in these pages. You'll be introduced to a succession of Clyde-built restaurants imbued with elements of Glasgow's distinctive personality; lively bistros, casual hideaways and maverick trend-setting venues; comfortable hangout spots that make neighbourhoods more interesting. We have you covered for breakfast, lunch, dinner and chips on the way home. Four years ago, I started writing about the best places and people in the city at Glasgowist.com. Regular restaurant visits and food conversations since then provide the foundation for this book, alongside lively insights from our online community. Opinions gathered from food writers and figures in the hospitality industry helped inform the final line-up. We start with the top ten restaurants, as voted by Glasgowist readers, then, the assembled recommendations covering everything you should eat in the city. There are around 2,000 restaurants in Glasgow. These are the ones that deserve your immediate attention.

Find more restaurant recommendations at Glasgowist.com

10. ROGANO

11 Exchange Pl, G1 3AN / 0141 248 4055 / roganoglasgow.com

It's an immersive experience. Place yourself in a room that stands at a particular point of time, while still embracing modern Glasgow hospitality. Attribute it to the time-capsule effect of escaping the busy streets around Buchanan Street, to be enveloped by the Art Deco style that was set when Rogano opened in 1935. Back then, the Cunard liner Queen Mary was being built on the Clyde, and that became the defining design influence. Rogano is not a classic curiosity, however, it's very much alive in the here and now. The restaurant retains an element of stardust from a bygone era. Henry Kissinger, Elizabeth Taylor, Bob Dylan and Rod Stewart are among the luminaries who have dined here. Not all at the same time. Had they arrived en masse, there would have been a serious discussion about who would sit at the prized table 16. This is considered the best table at Rogano as you have a sweeping view of the restaurant, and with the aid of mirrors you can see what's going on behind you at the door. Should you, a visiting celebrity or a tired shopper, wish to avoid anyone at the entrance, there's convenient access to the back door nearby. Martin Conner is now the Head Chef leading the kitchen, putting his own imprint on the menu with more venison and lamb dishes. A sushi platter is a recent addition. He previously worked for Six by Nico and for Hutchesons. Pass through the bar to the dining room with jazz notes floating in the background and linger for lunch.

Best Dish: Half lobster Thermidor with Frites (£27)

9. JULIE'S KOPITIAM

1109 Pollokshaws Rd, G41 3YG / 0141 237 9560 / fb.com/julieskopitiam

From Masterchef contestant to street food pioneer to established Pollokshaws Road favourite. Julie Lin MacLeod's star is very much in the ascendancy. Rarely a month goes by without an approving nod for her Shawlands Kopitiam (Malaysian for coffee shop) from visiting food critics. A new, bigger venue is coming in 2020 - we hear dumplings will be on the menu - while the current site continues to be one of the busiest food places in a particularly competitive part of the Glasgow culinary map. Much of the appeal comes from colourful, simple dishes that get straight to the point. Often consisting of just four or five carefully selected ingredients, they crackle and pop with flavour as chilli flakes and crispy onions are sprinkled on top of sambals, soys and rich curry sauces. Fried eggs and bowls of brown rice here taste more exciting than seems plausible, while the roti and curry dip is a satisfying, addictive snack that's become a mainstay on an otherwise constantly evolving menu. With the ever changing offering, a sensible starting point on a first visit is the nonya-style curry of the day, where seasonal Scottish produce is enlivened with the spices and know-how of Julie's Malaysian heritage to create comforting bowls. "It's fusion, in the best sense" as she puts it. This year there has been a popular residency at SWG3's Acid Bar. Expect more pop-ups and high levels of creativity. Readers say: "cool place with stunning food", "staff are really friendly, good value for money", "a fun experience".

Best Dish: Mamak Fried Chicken (£7)

8. THE BUTCHERSHOP BAR & GRILL

1055 Sauchiehall St, G3 7UD / 0141 339 2999 / butchershopglasgow.com

Serve the best steak and let people have fun. That was the short mission statement when James and Louise Rusk decided to open a neighbourhood restaurant in 2010. They've since added Hutchesons and The Spanish Butcher to their hospitality group - both of which go their own way but remain heavily influenced by that original mantra. Meanwhile, in the West End, The Butchershop Bar & Grill continues to attract an enthusiastic following. Exposed brick walls, cosy round leather booths. Regulars tell us they are interested in one thing. Sure, there is depth to the menu and some alluring signature dishes - glazed Iberican pork cheeks, we're looking at you - but the main event is easy to spot. It's the kind of big-time eating Glasgow folk revel in. Grass fed Scotch beef, hung on the bone and dry-aged for up to 45 days. They come from far and wide, congregating for fillets, sirloins, rib eyes, tomahawks and all the rest of the prime cuts. Enjoy with hand cut chips, bearnaise sauce and top with garlic prawns for the full experience. Onion rings and creamed spinach on the side. Outstanding local produce, prepared with skill and precision, served with a sense of occasion in a relaxed setting. Go with pals for dinner and sit near the window for views out towards University of Glasgow while you carve your way through your meal. Popular for Sunday roast with all the trimmings. Readers say: "exceptional food", "the best steak in Glasgow for sure", "a quality night out", "delicious menu and amazing wine".

Best Dish: Côte de Boeuf (£38)

7. TWO FAT LADIES AT THE BUTTERY

652 Argyle St / 0141 221 8188 / twofatladiesrestaurant.com

When discussing dining in Scotland, actress Kelly MacDonald told the New York Times: "I love Two Fat Ladies at The Buttery, one of the oldest restaurants in Glasgow, with dark-wood paneling and tartan upholstery. They do an amazing sole meunière". The best table is probably the alcove in the corner, ideal for indiscreet conversations over a leisurely lunch. Having said that, there's a Chef's Table built into the kitchen, where groups can gaup through glass as their meal is prepared. Ryan James started off on Dumbarton Road and then took over The Buttery thirteen years ago. He also has a city centre restaurant on Blythwood Street. The Buttery itself dates from 1870 – but it took a patient refurbishment and some culinary flair for it to retake its place among the best restaurants in the city. On one level, it's an old-school classic, but it could also be considered something of a hipster trendsetter as, it's fair to say, Two Fat Ladies liked Finnieston before it was cool. This is the type of place that is difficult to create, it has to evolve over time. A traditional dining room without being stuffy. If you took a date here, they would be impressed. The charming staff glide between tables and put guests at ease. There's a buzz of easy conversation. Tourists who visit The Buttery like what they find. "I think people should be very proud when they talk about Scotland's larder. Sometimes we don't say that loud enough" Ryan tells us. Tip: Always order the scallops starter.

Best Dish: Grilled Whole Lemon Sole Meuniere (£23)

6. UBIQUITOUS CHIP

12 Ashton Ln, G2 2ND / 0141 334 5007 / ubiquitouschip.co.uk

Ubiquitous Chip has become a byword for Glasgow cooking, in more ways than one. The venue's success is due to the efforts of the talented staff combined with the genial atmosphere generated by its faithful cadre of bohemian customers who come here to tell stories and eat stovies. The Chip is at the heart of that whole Ashton Lane scene – it practically invented it – and emblematic of the West End. A business crowd rubs shoulders with the arty set upstairs on the twinkling mezzanine level or in the restaurant. Students are brought here by parents to mark progress in their studies with red wine and a selection of dishes involving seasonal Scottish produce. There's a danger when you approach a restaurant enveloped in local mythology that expectations can be too high. Rest assured, there is fun to be had, and if you are interested in a dram of whisky and innovative Scottish cooking, you've come to the right place. The signature dish since 1971 has been The Chip's own venison haggis with champit tatties and neep cream. It is probably the only fixed point on a menu that changes regularly and varies between the restaurant and the brasserie. On our last visit we enjoyed Shetland mussels in white wine with chorizo, cyboes and cream (£7.95), Ramsay's pork belly, pippa potatoes, pancetta and duxelles (£14.95), with crowdie cheesecake, honey oats and strawberries (£6.45). Ubiquitous Chip is a dining destination with a strong sense of place and a big personality. Go to their Wee Whisky Bar after dinner.

Best Dish: Loin of Lamb, Ratatouille, Sherry jus (£28.95)

5. GAMBA

225A W George St / 0141 572 0899 / gamba.co.uk

Gamba: Simple Seafood Cooking is the title of chef Derek Marshall's cookbook and also his motto in the kitchen. From the East End of Glasgow, he left school with no qualifications and joined a youth training programme. It was the start of a culinary journey of discovery that would take him to the Channel Islands, the French Alps and Spain. Gamba turns 21 this year. It has held a 2 AA Rosettes rating since the first oyster was shucked, way back in 1998. The entire landscape of city restaurants has shifted over the last two decades, yet this smart high-achiever remains a reliable choice for our readers. "Let the ingredients shine" Derek says. He has an excellent relationship with Scotland's fishing community that allows Gamba to source the finest catch of the day. Menus are updated every six weeks to ensure the seasonality and quality of ingredients. However, new dishes always sit alongside Gamba classics that Derek knows his customers come back for time and again. Our own routine when visiting for dinner is to start with a bowl of foup - what Gamba call their fish soup, a finely balanced blend of Portland crabmeat, stem ginger, coriander and prawn dumplings. Monkfish and scallops for main course, cooked with ginger, spring onions, fish sauce and lemon. It's worth noting that their desserts are fairly spectacular, so order the wild honey and ginger cheesecake with dark berries and ask about their gin cocktails. Readers say: "My absolute favourite for seafood", "dinner is always a pleasure".

Best Dish: Isle of Gigha Halibut with Brown Shrimps (£24)

4. SIX BY NICO

1132 Argyle St, G3 8TD / 0141 334 5661 / sixbynico.co.uk

Judging by the naming convention at chef Nico Simeone's restaurants, he likes numbers. So, lets start with some. Six thousand customers book a table at his themed dining concept on Argyle Street every month. It operates at a 98% capacity Tuesday to Thursday and at full capacity on weekends. Six by Nico is a hit. A new Southside branch added 30 covers per service when it opened on Nithsdale Road in October. Here's how it works: a six-course tasting menu for £29, with a wine pairing option for £26 is created around an idea, place or memory. Experimental preparations cue nostalgic emotions, deconstruct a particular cuisine or pepper a series of small plates with pop culture references. The time limit on the restaurant creates an impetus to visit and also adds to the sense of occasion when you enjoy your meal. Enthusiastic staff introduce each dish as they are presented at the table. Pictures are taken for Instagram. The kitchen has served up Charlie and the Chocolate Factory treats, a particularly impressive Vietnamese street food menu, dishes inspired by the chippy and a throwback menu from the 1980s. After time runs out on one theme, Six by Nico simply moves on to a new story and set of flavours. We salute Nico's ambition and commitment to innovation. He is a Glasgow success story, taking Six by Nico to Edinburgh, Belfast, Manchester and most recently Liverpool. Readers say: "Our Finnieston favourite", "special every time", "can't get enough of these tasting menus".

Best Dish: Six course Tasting Menu (£29)

3. CAIL BRUICH

725 Gt Western Rd, G12 8QX / 0141 334 6265 / cailbruich.co.uk

Cail Bruich is known for beautiful food and an innovative approach to fine dining. The family-run restaurant and bar currently holds a 3 AA Rosette status and was included in the latest Michelin Guide, although they are inexplicably reluctant to present brothers Paul and Chris Charalambous with a star. When the Good Food Guide 2020 announced the best places to eat in the UK, Cail Bruich was included in the top 50 restaurants in the country. Last year the dining room was given a new look to mark the tenth anniversary of the Great Western Road stalwart. An impressive maître d' station – hewn from a trunk of fallen Scots lime by Tim Norman at GalGael Trust in Govan – is the first thing guests see when they arrive. The dining room and bar feature natural wood finishes and stripped-back brick walls, illuminated by quirky light fittings and tables brightened by fresh floral arrangements. They describe their core audience as ranging from "families toasting special occasions and celebratory affairs to an ever-growing audience of younger diners in search of quality, contemporary cuisine and select drinks". You can enjoy Scottish cuisine with a French influence. Menus rotate in harmony with the seasons. Produce arrives daily from local suppliers including Loch Fyne Sea Farms, Highland Game Company and Isle of Skye Shellfish. These ingredients are combined with ingredients provided by the kitchen's own garden and a team of foragers. Glasgowist readers compliment their confident cooking and attentive staff.

Best Dish: **Seasonal Tasting Menu (£65)**

2. THE GANNET

1155 Argyle St, G3 8TB / 0141 204 2081 / thegannetgla.com

A highly-regarded leader of the Glasgow restaurant new wave, The Gannet has attracted international attention for fine dining in a modern, casual setting. Ivan Stein and Peter McKenna are working chefs and owners: preparing dishes, organising ingredients, devising menus. Ivan is from London, Peter is Irish. Both gravitated towards Glasgow. They couldn't see a restaurant they wanted to work in. So they created their own in a vacant tenement building that had been derelict for almost a decade. With the help of architects and a significant amount of hard work, a stylish bar and restaurant was fashioned from the space. The food concept was born in the summer of 2012 on a trip to the Hebrides to source produce for their kitchen in the West End. By the end of the trip, they had met scallop divers, oyster growers, fishermen, smokers, farmers, game producers and some interesting characters. "We've put the time in" Peter says. "We've spent countless days travelling around Scotland in the the car, going to farms, visiting gamekeepers we had heard about". Now, there isn't a main ingredient in the restaurant that doesn't come direct from the source. "Every two weeks we get a side of beef, for instance. I know the farm that it comes from, what its been grazing on. We have total control over the product". The relationships the chefs have with local producers, combined with flair in the kitchen, is the basis of their success. Some of our favourite Glasgow meals have been enjoyed at The Gannet.

Best Dish: **Seasonal Tasting Menu (£45)**

1. OX AND FINCH

920 Sauchiehall St, G3 7TF / 0141 339 8627 / oxandfinch.com

Glasgowist readers have voted Ox and Finch as the best restaurant in the city right now. We arrive late on a Friday night and secure a table for six, shortly before the kitchen closes. Things are not winding down. Every other table is full. There's a pace and energy to Ox and Finch as staff move with a sense of purpose and dishes appear from the kitchen with precision. You come here for modern small plate dining. Assemble a selection of dishes, divide and conquer. The menu covers a lot of culinary ground. A myriad of influences and ingredients, some familiar, others surprising. The fact the kitchen can maintain impeccably high standards across such a selection is the greatest achievement of the restaurant team. It's a food wonderland. Some of our favourite dishes: venison, juniper and peppercorn carpaccio, hazelnuts and crowdie. Thai fish cakes, prik nam pla, lettuce wrappers and pickled salads. Charred leeks, poached egg and toasted almonds. Slow-cooked lamb shoulder, bulgur wheat, apricots, almonds and mint yoghurt. You get the picture. Dishes arrive and there's a blizzard of activity. Forks stake a claim as colourful morsels are shared. Plates move in every direction. It's a lively neighbourhood restaurant that celebrates food with an inspiring approach to cooking. Visit often. Readers say: "Delicious dishes. Always presented beautifully. Fab cocktails", "the food is always fantastic and great value", "amazing staff", "the menu is a tribute to Scotland".

Best Dish: Cod Cheek, Morcilla, Chorizo and Tomato (£7.50)

111 BY NICO

111 Cleveden Rd, G12 0JU / 0141 334 0111 / 111bynico.co.uk

Modou Diagme is Senegalese, but spent most of his early years in Spain. At the age of 18, he came over to Glasgow by himself with only £150 in his pocket. He slept rough for 10 days, then found shelter in a church that helps the homeless. Eventually he found a permanent place to stay. After a year of applying for jobs with no success, he stumbled across Nico Simeone's advert looking for kitchen porters. Over the last five years he has learned the fundamentals of cooking and proven himself to be a leader in the kitchen. Modou is Head Chef at 111 by Nico where his team are utterly committed to creating an enthralling dining experience. Guests at the West End restaurant are encouraged to sit back, relax and trust the kitchen as dish after dish are created from seasonal ingredients. Seldom the same dinner twice, the Trust concept menu begins with an amuse-bouche, then guests enjoy individual courses such as pasta, lamb, asparagus or fish without knowing the constituent ingredients and preparations in advance. The mysterious six course tasting menu ends on a sweet note with a rich dessert like pistachio panna cotta, compressed plum, mirabelle gel, crystallised oats and damson ice cream. A theatrical ten couse tasting menu is the latest innovation at the Cleveden Road venue on Fridays and Saturdays. The level of preparation, the effort that is invested in each course at 111 by Nico is extraordinary. The restaurant strives for higher things and hits every gastronomic mark.

Best Dish: Six Course Tasting Menu (£30)

A'CHALLTAINN

54 Calton Entry, G40 2SB / 0141 548 1338 / baadglasgow.com/achalltainn

A'Challtainn have always set out to shine a light on the best of Scottish produce. Some days, it shines particularly bright – the balcony of the restaurant looks out over the inside courtyard at BAaD. Encased in an arched glass roof, it's a natural suntrap. One of the few places it is acceptable to wear sunglasses indoors in the East End. The wine list and menu have been finessed in recent months, with new seasonal dishes added to the mix - chargrilled octopus with ratatouille and sauce or hand dived scallops with South Indian spiced puy lentils are perfect for sharing. In our minds, seafood is still the star of the show. Take note: The lobsters they source are big, beautiful heavyweights that can take all challengers. The Barras Art and Design Centre, which is home to A'Challtainn, has found a renewed sense of purpose, bringing together artists, performers and street food vendors at weekends. Promoters Ricky Scoular and Brian Traynor, sensing a burgeoning appetite for the best Scottish seafood and a rising East End, opened the restaurant here in 2016. In doing so, they began to dilute invisible lines that separated this area from the rest of the city centre. Brian tells us: "We want people to come in and realise that you can still have top quality service, great local produce, good imaginative cooking, ideas throughout the menu, but also a laid-back environment. It's very accessible to anybody and everybody. All are welcome". A lively and stylish spot, with an excellent music policy.

Best Dish: Torched Mackerel, Orange and Fennel Salad (£8)

ACCENTO CAFE

6 Claremont St, G3 7HA / 0141 258 3830

Accento is a a delighful family-run eatery, established on the outer fringe of
the Finnieston food scene by Alessandra Pili, her sister Francesca and brother-
in-law Riccardo Pireddu. They arrived in Glasgow in 2014 and decided to bring
a taste of their homeland with them by introduciong us all to some Sardinian
flavour. We are very glad they did. Their glorious panini are stuffed with cured
meats, melting cheeses and piled high with imported or local ingredients.
There's homemade soup and cakes to go. Big Franco is their champion panino
with chicken Milanese, lettuce, tomatoes and mayo. Named after Francesca
and Alessandra's dad, it has become a famous name in local lunchtimes.

Best Dish: **Big Franco (£3.95)**

ACID BAR

100 Eastvale Pl, G3 8QG / 0141 337 1731/ swg3.tv

If you enjoy dining on multicultural cuisine while drinking cocktails and gazing out at street art from a stylish restaurant that feels like a communal diner housed in a cool gallery, then this is the place. Exciting things happen at Acid Bar, within the burgeoning network of studio, warehouse venue and office space thriving by the Clyde at SWG3. It's a cool cafe by day, where restless creatives study their iPhones and sip on coffee from The Steamie Coffee Roasters. Then at night and at weekends top local talent takeover the kitchen for dazzling showcases. It's already been an impressive guest roster, including Ox and Finch, Cail Bruich and Julie's Kopitiam. The rolling restaurant residencies are set to be an exciting part of the local food scene for 2020.

Best Dish: Menu changes for each residency

ALCHEMILLA

1126 Argyle St, G3 8TD / 0141 337 6060/ thisisalchemilla.com

There's been changes in the kitchen but no drop in quality at Alchemilla. It remains the place to go for simple cooking with clever ingredient combinations. Smoked mussels and charred leeks. Salted onglet, pickled clams and spinach. Artichokes, carrots, cauliflower, girolles mushrooms and lots of herbs feature regularly. "This food isn't intricate or precise. It is not made to be photographed. It is designed to be fabulous to eat", says Jay Rayner. It's a dream restaurant for vegetarians. with a strong Mediterranean and Middle-Eastern influence. Even the little things can be a delight here. Is it possible to get excited about a tomato salad or a plate of bortolli beans? It is. It really is. Remember them for a fresh, rewarding, good-value lunch.

Best Dish: **Octopus, Burnt Clementine and Chicory (£8.50)**

AMBER REGENT

50 West Regent St, G2 2RA / 0141 331 1655 / amberregent.com

The Chung family have run Amber Regent since 1988, blending Scottish produce and Cantonese flavours. Seafood and shellfish remain at the heart of the menu, with signature dishes including scallops and king prawns in XO sauce. There's also a range of classic meat dishes such as their aromatic crispy lamb, or the much lauded belly of pork served with fluffy Chinese bao and rich hoisin sauce. They recently refurbished, giving the dining room a bright, contemporary style while retaining some of the familiar aspects of the restaurant over the last three decades. The most obvious change is the increased the capacity; including the addition of a smart cocktail bar and private dining room. Billy Connolly has been a weekend visitor.

Best Dish: **Deep Fried Szechuan Chicken (£15.95)**

THE ANCHOR LINE

12-16 St Vincent Pl, G1 2DH / 0141 248 1434/ theanchorline.co.uk

A business-friendly dining room and cocktail bar, immaculate and plush, in a striking building on St Vincent Street, close to George Square. Big windows and lots of light. Space to move around. A lot to look at. The distinguishing local touches are the many pictures and fixtures covering the walls that depict the opulent world of transatlantic travel on grand steamships – a company called Anchor Line operated routes between Glasgow and New York in the early 1900s, they had an office on Union Street. The bric-a-brac and period posters are endearing. There's a strong surf and turf element to the menu. Order grilled oysters Rockefeller with spinach, garlic butter and lemon or a ribeye steak, direct from a Josper grill. Make it a regular port of call.

Best Dish: **Lobster and King Prawn Mac n' Cheese (£21.95)**

BAFFO PIZZA

1377 Argyle St, G3 8AF / 0141 583 0000 / baffo.co.uk

Baffo Pizza and Birra on Argyle Street, right across the road from Kelvingrove Art Gallery, is home to the Mezzo Metro pizza in Glasgow. Owner Francesco Longo, was on a trip to Verona with his family when he fell in love with a little pizza place at the end of the road serving Italy's finest by the metre and hatched a plan to bring that to Glasgow. Baffo takes pride in their food and work to create a relaxed atmosphere in the restaurant. In addition to pizza, you can also find a selection of street food sides, cut to order antipasti, focaccia, traditional and modern bruschetta and a grand selection of pasta. Tiramisu is made to an old family recipe. Grab a booth with views out towards Kelvingrove Art Gallery and Museum.

Best Dish: **Nonno Ciccio Pizza (£8)**

BAR BRETT

321 Great Western Rd, G4 9HR / barbrett.co.uk

Trundle through traffic along Great Western Road and you will notice some new arrivals. It has has been a particularly notable year for this stretch of the West End, with a steady stream of bars and restaurants making their debut. In this case, the talented team at the award-winning Cail Bruich, further down the street, are behind the recently-opened and stylishly put-together wine bar beside Barrington Drive. It quietly arrived without much fanfare over the summer, unrecognisable from what was previously here. Inside, Brett is a subtle but slick mix of green ceramic tiles, industrial style shelving, bare brick walls, comfy high stools, with a compact open kitchen as a centrepiece. This is a wine bar where the food is front and centre. Brett's short menu offers daily changing sharing plates. Expect a rolling roster of fish, meat, shellfish, cheese, charcuterie and vegetable dishes. Clean and simple cooking. Strong flavour combinations. Homemade pickles and emulsions. Notable suppliers including Peelham Farm, East Coast Cured, Loch Fyne Oysters, Locavore organic vegetables and Mellis cheeses. The wines, selected from sustainable small wine growers from across Europe, are also rotated regularly. Bookings can be made for the mezzanine, but we like sittting at the bar counter top with a clear view of the chefs at work and wine near at hand. Watch out for specials or days when the chefs are trying something different in the kitchen - a beef Wellington on a Wednesday has been a recent theme.

Best Dish: **Toulouse Sausage and White Bean Cassoulet (£10)**

BASTA PIZZA

561 Dumbarton Rd, G11 6HU / 0141 339 8698 / bastapizza.com

The foundation of the menu at Basta is imported Polselli flour, Strianese tomatoes and extra virgin olive oil from Italy. Plus fresh produce sourced as close to home as possible, including from the local Sandy Road Community Garden. After that, anything goes. No flavour combination is considered too outlandish. If it works, it's on the menu. Meanwhile, Prince or CHIC is usually on the stereo. They want to bring the joy back into pizza with interesting toppings and an easy-going vibe in the dining room. Chef owner Jane Chalmers says "we've fairly traditional pizzas on the menu. The more popular ones are the specials that we work on in the kitchen. Our first was Irn Bru ham and fresh pineapple, finished with a blow torch. Our version of a Partick Hawaiian."

Best Dish: Ricotta Cream Chicken Pizza (£10)

BATTLEFIELD REST

55 Battlefield Rd, G42 9JL / 0141 636 6955 / battlefieldrest.co.uk

Built as a particularly impressive-looking tram station in 1915, this local landmark fell into a state of disrepair before being rescued through restoration, led by businessman Marco Giannasi. He opened Battlefield Rest, an Italian bistro, here in 1994. The same head chef is still here after 25 years, with Marino Donati leading the team in the kitchen. Remarkable. They enjoy crossing Scottish and Italian flavours. "We made some cannelloni haggis one day and then customers kept ordering it, so that became a signature dish" Marco says. They buy cured meats and pasta from North Tuscany. Service is prompt and warm, conversation flows as easily as the wine, people relax and take time over their meal. A local favourite.

Best Dish: **Cod Gnocchi (£14.90)**

BIBIMBAP

3 West Nile St, G1 2PR / 0141 221 6111 / bibimbap-glasgow.com

Bibimbap takes its name from Korea's favourite comfort food. It is served as a bowl of warm white rice topped with namul (sautéed and seasoned vegetables) and gochujang (chili pepper paste), soy sauce, a fried egg and other ingredients like beef or pork. This year, it has been their Korean Fried Chicken that's been getting all the attention. You can order a tray of plump wings in crispy batter, served in three different sizes. Cover in spicy sauce and share with your pals. Other stand-out dishes include bulgogi beef rice bowls, Janchigugsu Korean carding noodles, clam stock with egg courgettes & chilli sauce and pork belly rice roll with spring onion and lettuce. Visit for cocktails, sake and beats at the weekend.

Best Dish: **Traditional Korean Fried Chicken (£11.50)**

BIBI'S CANTINA

599-601 Dumbarton Rd G11 6HY / 0141 579 0179/ bibiscantina.co.uk

The interior is comfortable, colourful and kitsch. A neighbourhood hangout with a bombastic selection of Latin American delicacies, the menu leans on Mexican flavours to make an impact. Bibi's has carved out their own special place in the affections of Partick diners over the last decade. On our last visit, we took a seat and ordered a round of margaritas. It's a tight fit in the dining room, watching the staff glide between tables and moving chairs is an education in agile service. Start with gambas con chorizo – prawn and chorizo skewers in a rich Cajun butter. Star of the show among the main dishes? Oven baked enchiladas with chicken and beans, a spicy sauce and Mexican cheese, served with coriander rice

Best Dish: **Coca Cola Beef Tostados (£12.95)**

BILSON ELEVEN

10 Annfield Pl, G31 2XQ / 0141 554 6259 / bilsoneleven.co.uk

Fine dining in Dennistoun. Bilson Eleven has a wonderful homely feel. A quality restaurant where you can be comfortable. Don't quite kick your shoes off, but feel free to settle into things. It's over three years now since they opened on Annfield Place, a row of townhouses that sits overlooking the junction of Bellgrove Street and Duke Street. When we first visited, we mused that the East End has seldom figured in Glasgow's culinary highlights in recent years. Since then, Bilson Eleven has been included in the Michelin Guide, with the cooking described as "interesting and original with a playful edge". Chef-owner Nick Rietz, who worked in Two Fat Ladies before setting out on his own, also had a recipe included in The Glasgow and West Coast Cook Book last year, which is arguably a bigger deal. From the start, Nick and his wife Liz's plan was to run a small but ambitious neighbourhood restaurant. They now serve five or eight course tasting menus or vegetarian menus - still something of a niche offering in Glasgow, but one that should be encouraged. There's a bit of theatre to it all. A performance from the chefs in the kitchen, building up the meal, dish by dish, to a satisfying crescendo. Then there is the opportunity for regular interactions with the servers who present and explain the dishes. Ask questions. Order wine. Plus you can have a bit of a blether with your pal between courses. Visit the charming culinary cocoon of Bilson Eleven and experience confident cooking that showcases exceptional local produce.

Best Dish: Tasting Menu (from £45)

BO & BIRDY

11 Blythswood Sq, G2 4AD / 0141 240 1633 / boandbirdy.com

Opening night set the tone for the glamorous Bo & Birdy. Invited guests enjoying new cocktails along with impressive dishes from the first menu were unexpectedly joined by Hugh Jackman – we're told he ate a pie after his performance at The Hydro. Ariana Grande, Billy Connolly, Michael Bublé and Christina Aquilera have all been recent visitors. The renovation of the dining room, to your left as you enter the Kimpton Blythswood Square Hotel, has created more of a feature of the Georgian building's large windows. It is as stylish a restaurant as you will find anywhere in the city. When the sun is shining, the whole space is flooded with light, reflecting off modern light fittings and assorted crystal decanters. Under the culinary guidance of the first female Executive Head Chef of a luxury hotel in Scotland, Gillian Matthews, signature dishes include the St Andrews Farmhouse cheddar macaroni cheese, Roast St Bride's chicken leg, gnocchi and king oyster mushrooms along with a delightfully rich Highland wagyu burger. The slogan here is "from farm to fabulous". Usually we would roll our eyes at such sentiments, but they do have a point. Our current favourite is their starter of beetroot tartare, apple, hazelnut, Lanark Blue cheese and leaves. A carefully balanced concotion of Caledonian tinged ingredients. Over £1 million was spent on creating the 146-cover restaurant, which debuted in April. One of the best openings of the year, Bo & Birdy is all set to fly high in 2020.

Best Dish: Highland Wagyu Burger with Smoked Bacon (£16)

BREAD MEATS BREAD

104 St Vincent St, G2 5UB / 0141 249 9898 / breadmeatsbread.com

We are at the burger crossroads. The much-maligned fast food staple has been elevated to a higher place and competition is fierce across the city. On St Vincent Street, Bread Meats Bread stares down all rivals from close quarters. Their high-impact combinations includes the ridiculously indulgent Luther Burger - a double smashed burger with American cheese, candied bacon, spicy beefy mayo and crispy fried onions inside a grilled glazed ring donut to turn the taste levels up to eleven. It's food to put a smile on your face. Bread Meats Bread also serve up big flavours from Great Western Road. Their menu includes gluten free and halal options. Order a portion of caramelised sweet potato fries, with maple syrup, cayenne pepper and coconut. A sensational side.

Best Dish: **Mustard Fried Cali Burger (£8.50)**

BRIAN MAULE AT CHARDON D'OR

176 West Regent St, G2 4RL / 0141 248 3801 / brianmaule.com

Whenever Glasgow's best chefs are mentioned, Brian Maule is invariably near the top of the list. Hard-working and talented, his restaurant on West Regent Street has been showered with awards and continues to provide the highest standard of fine dining in the city. Maule is a former head chef at le Gavroche and well-respected in the industry, endorsed by Michel Roux Jr who says: "Our eleven years at le Gavroche showed me time and time again what he was capable of and it is a thrill to see these standards maintained at le Chardon D'or". A fierce advocate for Scottish produce, expect preparations of smoked haddock, scallops and Scotch lamb on the menu. Look out for their Gin Experience and Lunch events that take place regularly.

Best Dish: Roast Duck Breast (£29.95)

CAFE D'JACONELLI

570 Maryhill Rd, G20 7EE / 0141 946 1124

It's old-fashioned, but that's the way we like it. They pretty much got things right from the start, opening in 1924 and renovating in 1951 - the last time they changed their look. A fixed point on Maryhill Road, they serve up haddock and chips, macaroni and cheese or a proper big breakfast fry up to cure hangovers. Burgers are served on crispy Mortons rolls. There will be days you will crave the familiar, traditional hospitality offfered at Jaconelli's. The most exciting part of the menu is the ice cream, drizzled in sauce, and classic sundaes. Stick a song on the jukebox and sink into one of the booths. The Ewan McGregor milkshake scene in Trainspotting was filmed here and the cafe featured in Tutti Frutti starring Robbie Coltrane.

Best Dish: **Macaroni and Cheese (£3.70)**

CAFE GANDOLFI

64 Albion St, G1 1NY / 0141 552 6813/ cafegandolfi.com

Seumas MacInnes arrived at Cafe Gandolfi in 1983 to peel potatoes and chop red cabbage and carrots. By 1995, he'd been a kitchen-porter, manager and co-owner until Cafe Gandolfi's founder, Iain Mackenzie, passed the flame on. Seumas' family connections to the Isle of Barra has informed his approach to food and helped create one of our favourite places in the city. Cafe Gandolfi boasts a bar upstairs and a separate city centre restaurant, Gandolfi Fish. They take their cooking seriously and offer a relaxed haven for long lunches or fun evenings with friends. We love the pictures of old Glasgow cafes that hang on the wall. Gandolfi is part of a long tradition. The furniture, created by artist Tim Stead, has been a fixture here since they opened in 1979.

Best Dish: **Stornoway Black Pudding and Pancakes (£8.90)**

CAFE STRANGE BREW

1082 Pollokshaws Rd, G41 3XA / 0141 440 7290

Good morning Shawlands. Cafe Strange Brew is waiting for you. How does waffles with candied orange, chilli chocolate ganache, whipped cream, marmalade gel, and chopped hazelnuts sound? One of the most Instagrammed food places in the city. Beautiful presentation, big portions and full-on flavours. Owner and chef Laurie MacMillan has redefined Glasgow's brunch scene, establishing an enthusiasting following at this Southside gem. Go to start your day with genuine local hospitality, delicious sourdough toast, picture-perfect poached eggs, crispy bacon and rich slices of black pudding served in slick surroundings. Bobby Gillespie is a fan. Remember to buy a chocolate brownie at the counter to take home with you.

Best Dish: **Turkish Eggs (£6.25)**

CAFEZIQUE

66 Hyndland St, G11 5PT / 0141 339 7180 / cafezique.com

Owner Mhairi Taylor's family have had a strong influence on her food philosophy. Her grandfather was known as Zique - his real name was Donald MacGregor - and her cafe is named for him. Her husband Dick Lewis is a farmer and most of the meat they use is supplied by his farm. Fantastic French toast is our choice for weekend brunch. In the evening take your pick from hearty dishes like yoghurt marinated lamb shank, pan roasted pork chop or soy braised duck leg and tahini puy lentals with olive tapenade. There's also plenty of colourful vegetables, salad and lighter food. Striking black and white screen prints hanging on stone walls set the scene in a relaxed, buzzy neighbourhood place that stands out from the crowd. They recently opened a bakery nearby.

Best Dish: **Spiced Chick Pea Curry (£13)**

CATCH

27 Gibson St, G12 8NU / 0141 370 8181 / catchfishandchips.co.uk

The idea arrived fully formed. "Open a high end, quality fish and chip experience. One that shows off the seafood of Scotland". As Giancarlo Celino grew up, his family had fish and chip shops, before they sold up and went into the wider restaurant industry. Like many of us, he retains fond memories of this glorious Glasgow favourite dish.That was the inspiration to open his own restaurant. The first Catch was in Giffnock then they took on the West End with this sophisticated Gibson Street chippy. They have been recommended in the Michelin Guide and named Best Seafood Restaurant by the National Fish & Chip Awards in 2017. Expect lobster, halibut, langoustine tails and old fashioned fish finger butties.

Best Dish: **Grilled Chilli King Prawn (£6.95)**

CELINO'S

235 Dumbarton Rd, G11 6AB / 0141 341 0311 / celinos.com

Celino's Italian Delicatessen Café and Pizzeria was opened in 1982 by Natalino Celino. It remains a local favourite on Alexandra Parade. A second trattoria in Partick arrived in 2017 and it has carried on the family's success in local hospitality. A nine metre long deli counter is a treasure trove of Italian gastronomy, loaded with charcuterie, artisan cheeses, fresh pasta, Italian bread, pizza and arancini, Sicilian pastries, cakes and ice cream. In the restaurant, diners can tuck into Italian classics for breakfast, lunch or dinner, often with a Scottish twist, like Capesante Alla Scozia - Fresh seared local scallops on a bed of Stornoway black pudding topped with a white wine and cream sauce. Named Best Deli Cafe at the Scottish Italian Awards.

Best Dish: **Carbonara Originale (£12)**

CHAAKOO BOMBAY CAFE

79 St Vincent St, G2 5TF/ 0141 229 0000/ chaakoo.co.uk

Chaakoo Bombay Cafe stands out from the crowd on St Vincent Street. The concentration of chain restaurants and burger joints on the stretch between Queen Street and Hope Street engenders fierce competition but little diversity. The intriguing idea here is to emulate the original Bombay cafes that were opened by Iranian immigrants to India in the 19th Century. In terms of decor, there's nods to the restaurant's cultural influences with prints, pictures and slogans dotted around the room. Delve into the Irani kebab menu for marinated smoked meats cooked on khule, robata and tandoor type grills to give them a distinctive taste. Surround your selection with freshly baked naan bread, Indian salads, fragrant rice and samosas.

Best Dish: **Kerala Monkfish (£9.95)**

COIA'S CAFE

473-477 Duke St, G31 1RD / 0141 554 3822 / coiascafe.co.uk

Known across the city, generations of the same family have built a business that's become emblematic of the Dennistoun area and has moved with the times. Italian and American influences in the food are infused with a powerful sense of local identity. A lively gathering place where you will be looked after. You'll always find something you like on the menu. If you are lucky, you'll find something you love. On our last visit we ordered tagliatelle with Italian sausage and porcini mushrooms. There's an increasing number of options nearby but a visit to Coia's brings with it an added element of conversation and a friendly atmosphere that's reassuring. This is a real Glasgow place. A landmark cafe on Duke Street since 1928.

Best Dish: **Linguine Alla Pescatora (£17.95)**

CRABSHAKK

1114 Argyle St, G3 8TD / 0141 334 6127 / crabshakk.com

Crabshakk have been serving cracking good food for the last ten years, blazing a trail for simple seafood dishes done well. It is an important part of the Glasgow food story. This is the fish place that inspired other chefs to look to Finnieston. It had a transformational effect on the area and remains a lynchpin for the local scene. It wears it all with an easy-going nature. A straight-forward menu is filled with crab, squid and scallops. Oysters, a fish supper and their Fruits de Mer platter for two have been available since day one. After his own visit, Michael Deacon said in The Telegraph: "The menu reads like pretty much the entire cast list of Finding Dory". We usually look for grilled langoustines in the evenings, one of the finest dishes you can order in the city of Glasgow. Study the specials board. That's where you're going to find the real catch of the day. We picked out a plate of bulbous, perfectly grilled octopus, served on a tasty mix of lentils and chorizo on our last visit. Glasgow has access to a dazzling supply of fresh seafood and here the flavours are showcased in a compact, buzzing restaurant with a laidback vibe and cheerful service. It gets very busy before concerts at The Hydro and it is fun to join in if you don't mind eating your seafood at close quarters to your fellow diners. David Beckham left suitably impressed after popping in for lunch. He ordered a kilo of mussels and a lobster. Grab a seat at the bar for a glass of wine and a meandering chat.

Best Dish: **Monkfish Cheek Scampi (£14.95)**

DENNISTOUN BAR-B-QUE

585 Duke St, G31 1PY / 0141 237 7200 / jaybes.co

Dennistoun is attracting attention. The past year has brought more tangible reasons to hang out in this part of town. It's more a case of filling in the gaps around the existing mix than a takeover. A slow, steady sea-change. Bookies, booze shops and barbers remain prevalent on Duke Street. There's also burgers. You'd almost describe Dennistoun Bar-B-Que as a diner. The food has American sensibilities but the attitude is pure Glasgow. It's a strong mix. Order at the counter, take your food home or find a place in the clutter of small tables. Gather lots of napkins - this is messy eating - and dig in. Their locally-sourced meats are smoked in-house using imported Texas oak. Try the Nutella barbecue ribs and imported soft drinks.

Best Dish: **Columbia Burger (£11)**

THE DHABBA

44 Candleriggs, G1 1LD / 0141 553 1249 / thedhabba.com

Chef JD Tewari has cooked for ministerial and presidential banquets as well as being a personal chef to the Prime Minister of India. You'll now find him presiding over the kitchen at The Dhabba, where they create North Indian cuisine inspired by traditional roadside diners in one of the Merchant City's most entertaining restaurants. There's no compromises when it comes to herbs or spices, igniting a local passion for fiery flavours and a whole new palate of exotic tastes. The Dhabba caters for vegans and all their recipes are nut free. Cooking from their earthenware pottery tandoor oven uses slow burning wood charcoal to prepare healthy bread, marinated meat or vegetable dishes. It is an experience that's had folk returning time and again since they opened in 2002.

Best Dish: **Boti Kabab Badami (£15.95)**

Be

Analytical.
Insightful.
Opinionated.

Be a Herald Subscriber.

- Advert-Light access to our website (meaning 80% faster loading pages!)
- Access to a full digital replica of the newspaper every day
- Access to our archives
- Access to Premium content
- Plus access to our apps

www.heraldscotland.com/subscribe

DUMPLING MONKEY

121 Dumbarton Rd, G11 6PR / 0141 583 8300 / dumplingmonkey.com

Where the East meets the West End. That's been Dumpling Monkey's motto since this stripped-back Chinese restaurant opened in 2013. It's not much to look at, but the food is immense. Students in particular are absolutely besotted with the place. They were the first in Glasgow to specialise in dumplings and steamed buns, the bang-on-trend Asian bites that are now a regular occurence on street food influenced menus. Serving authentic dishes inspired by Northern Chinese cuisine, they specialise in potstickers, noodles and wonton soups. For drinks there is a fine range of bubble coffees and fruit teas. The menu is long, detailed and available for delivery direct to your living room. A portion of ten satisfying, plump pork dumplings costs a fiver.

Best Dish: **Beef and Carrot Bao Zi Steamed Bun (£1.50)**

DURTY VEGAN BURGER CLUB

994 Argyle St, G3 8LU / 07377 911773 / fb.com/dvbcglasgow

Self-styled Mad Chef Danny McLaren has joined the food scene on Argyle Street. He regularly talks about waking up in the morning with all kinds of ideas for recipes. For the last two years or so he's been refining an outstanding vegan burger and other dishes. Now these creations have a permanent home. The team work to break down preconceptions about plant based food and create a buzz at lunchtimes. They've recently expanded their opening times to include evenings. "You need to put all your skills, your experiences and your passions into one place. That's exactly what we are doing with Durty Vegan Burger Club" Danny says. Go help save the planet while enjoying a cocoa and vanilla chocolate, jam-filled donut.

Best Dish: **Barbecue jackfruit B12 Burger (£13)**

EL PERRO NEGRO

966 Argyle St, G3 8LU / 0141 248 2875/ el-perro-negro.com

Dreamed up by Nick Watkins who started out with events that established demand for their Top Dog burger - a rare-breed beef patty topped with slices of rare-breed bacon, then bone marrow and roquefort butter, caramelised onions and black truffle mayo on a toasted brioche bun. It's a thing of beauty. A neat little permanent base opened in Finnieston with backing from The Gannet co-owners and chefs Peter McKenna and Ivan Stein. Nick went to London and defeated competition from Gordon Ramsay's Bread Street Kitchen and some of the leading restaurants in the country to win the National Burger of the Year title in February 2019. Organic and free range beef from Peelham Farm. You'll also find El Perro Negro on Woodlands Road.

Best Dish: **Top Dog Burger (£10.50)**

ERROL'S HOT PIZZA

379 Victoria Rd, G42 8RZ / 0141 423 0559

A tiny place, they opened with little fanfare and quickly attracted attention for a selection of New York style pizzas. Thick crusts, crispy base, wide slices for folding, bubbling cheese and a sprinkling of toppings. There's a bit of a dive bar style to Errol's, with odd artwork arranged on dark walls and a buzzy nighttime vibe. "Walk-ins only, takeaway when possible". At busy times you will have to wait your turn to grab a spot inside. The pizza chefs were previously at Alchemilla so they know about balancing flavours. They all live locally and decided to create the kind of evening place they would like to hangout. There are some interesting small plates on the menu featuring broccoli, chilli, artichokes, garlic and lemon.

Best Dish: **Sausage and Fennel Pizza (£12)**

EUSEBI

152 Park Rd, G4 9HB / 0141 648 9999 / eusebideli.com

It all started just over 40 years ago when the Eusebi family opened their first deli in Shettleston, importing products from small artisan makers across Italy. They moved to the west end in 2015 and opened a restaurant and deli on the corner of Gibson Street and Park Road, across from the entrance to Kelvingrove Park. Expect freshly made Italian dishes along with imported pastas, wine, cheeses and meats to take home with you. Giovanna Eusebi proudly carries on the culinary traditions started by her grandfather. The local breakfast club take over the terrace seats in the morning. Order the cacio pepe royale for brunch. Soft scrambled eggs, Roman style with smoked salmon, pecorino and black pepper, served on toasted sourdough.

Best Dish: **Fettucine Black Truffle (£19)**

EVOO

112 Cowcaddens Rd, G4 0HL / 0141 332 4032 / evooglasgow.co.uk

Glasgow's such a walkable city, it only takes a place to be one or two streets from the main throng and it feels off the beaten track. EVOO hides in plain sight at the northernmost tip of the centre, but no more than 100 metres from The Theatre Royal and other bars and restaurants, including it's own Scottish sister restaurant, Ardnamurchan. It's Extra Virgin Olive Oil by both name and nature inside this bright, white space with a casual vibe and eye-catching small plates. Freshly baked focaccia is served with some olive oil for dipping, and much of the menu is drizzled or oven baked in the stuff. Think well-executed favourites from Italy, Spain and Greece. The quality of ingredients is high, their sheer range is impressive. EVOO is worth the walk.

Best Dish: **17 Month Aged San Daniele Proscuitto Crudo (£5)**

THE FINNIESTON

1125 Argyle St, G3 8ND / 0141 222 2884 / thefinniestonbar.com

It was built as a drovers inn, one that Rob Roy MacGregor is said to have frequented. As time went by, the distinctive, small blue building was enveloped by the city of Glasgow and dwarfed by neighbouring tenements. A cabinet maker, a hotelier and a dairy farmer called this address home before, in 2011, The Finnieston opened as a seafood and cocktail destination. Eyebrows were raised. The place didn't have much culinary company back then, on an under-populated stretch of Argyle Street. Soon, their success would help trigger an influx of new bistros, bars and beards to the area. Inside the two-storey building, which has the feel of a seaside tavern, you'll find cosy booths under old wooden beams. A small garden is out the back, where we sometimes like to sip gin in the evenings. They have over 60 different varieties of gin behind the bar here. A lot of whisky too. Scotland's shorelines are showcased on the menu, with clams, scallops and mussels sitting alongside salmon, haddock and halibut, all sustainably sourced. The restaurant serves lunch and a seasonally adjusted a la carte dinner menu, with brunch added at weekends. Choose some gorgeous Isle of Gigha oysters, finished with a dash of Bloody Mary or gin and tonic granita. Order a whole Pittenween lobster if you are feeling fancy. The popular Finnie Fish burger is a half fillet of haddock, served with pickles, iceberg and tartar sauce. Once a trend-setting new upstart, The Finnieston is now a celebrated flag-bearer for the local food scene.

Best Dish: Isle of Barra Monkfish Steak (£22)

FINSBAY FLATIRON

160 Woodlands Rd, G3 6LF / 0141 332 3399 / facebook.com/FinsbayFF

A lively steak joint with a strong rugby connection. It opened in time for the Six Nations last year. Two of the team behind the venture are Alastair Kellock, who played for Scotland and Glasgow Warriors, and Stuart Hogg, who has more than 50 caps for the national team. It's a sister venue to Finsbay, the cafe, bar and restaurant in Milngavie. When it first appeared, it was considered a pop-up, set to last a couple of months. But then Scotland beat France and England and by the time the celebrations died down FF had become a permanent fixture on Woodlands Road. We like their rum collection, weekend brunches and hearty Sunday roasts, served with live acoustic music. Fun Fact: This place was previously The Halt Bar, where the members Belle and Sebastian first met.

Best Dish: Spiced Flat Iron Steak (£10)

THE FISH PEOPLE CAFE

350A Scotland St, G5 8QF / 0141 429 8787 / thefishpeoplecafe.co.uk

When Andy Bell and family looked at the adjacent industrial cafe to their southside fishmongers that had lain dormant and disused for a number of years, they saw an opportunity. Seizing the chance to try something new, they embarked on a substantial renovation of the neighbouring unit. Resplendent in the French bistro décor that you see today, The Fish People Cafe opened in September 2012. The restaurant cooking style consists of simple, classic Scottish dishes, often with an international influence, like tandoori sea bass and Shetland salmond sashimi. The menu features Tarbert landed monkfish, Cumbrae rock oysters, which can be enjoyed at the marble oyster bar, Greenland shrimp and hand-dived Barra scallops.

Best Dish: **Grilled Lemon Sole (£22.50)**

FIVE MARCH

140 Elderslie St, G3 7QF / 0141 573 1400 / fivemarch.co.uk

Five March has a slick style bar look but laidback suburban sensibilities. Your favourite local DJ probably eats here. It sits on the edge of Kelvingrove Park, near to Charing Cross. This cool wee gastropub is run by Joanna Nethery and Kevin Small former employees of The Admiral and Distill, which is a good meeting of minds when it comes to creating a space for friends, food, drinks and good times. Try pork schnitzel or fried chicken wedged between Freedom Bakery sourdough bread or put together a range of small plates. Vegetarians will be impressed. Other options involve seared scallops, torched salmon and pork croquette. Mezcal and tequila feature heavily on the cocktail menu. Take to the comfortable terrace outside when the sun is shining.

Best Dish: **Roast Cauliflower and Pickled Grapes (£8)**

GLORIOSA

1321 Argyle St, G3 8AB / 0141 334 0594

An early contender for the most significant new restaurant opening of 2020? Rosie Healey, the founding chef of Achemilla, returns to Glasgow after a spell in London at Padella Pasta in Shoreditch. Expect immaculately prepared vegetable and pasta dishes on Argyle Street, with fish and meat plates from the wood-fired oven. Gloriosa serve large and traditional dishes: "It's all about generous cooking. It's not fine dining but I want people to feel like they are gettng a real treat and that they're being cared for". Derek Sutherland of Firebird approached Rosie with the opportuity and is a partner in the business. Lily Brown, formerly restaurant manager at Legs in London's Hackney, is a third partner, leading the front-of-house and the wine operation. One to watch.

Best Dish: Wood Roasted Cardamon Poisson With Harissa

GNOM

758 Pollokshaws Rd, G41 2AE / 0141 258 2949 / fb.com/gnomfood

Progressive street food outfit Chompsky spawned Strathbungo eatery Gnom. The original inspiration for chefs was the writings of American philosopher and political activist Noam Chomsky combined with an internationalist approach to cooking that encompassed Korean fried chicken, Jamaican goat stew and Taiwanese bao buns. They traded pop-ups for a permanent home on Pollokshaws Road and finessed their daytime offering, recently launching a new evening menu, available Wednesday to Sunday. You should still expect a playful, experimental and global approach to food from the kitchen, but dishes are increasingly sophisticated and impressive. Think stuffed Thai sardines with tamarind, potted smoked salmon and porchetta.

Best Dish: **Ricotta Gnocchi (£8)**

HALLOUMI

697 Pollokshaws Rd, G41 2AB / 0141 423 6340 / halloumiglasgow.co.uk

Halloumi look to Athens for inspiration. Greek flavours shine through from the menu, crafted with modern Mediterranean sensibilities. Visit with friends who like to share their food. This is leisurely, small plate dining, with plenty of opportunities to interrupt your procession of dishes for cocktails or wine. Good for date night. Gyros: difficult to pronounce, easy to eat. A fresh, light, toasted flat bread stuffed with grilled pork, chicken or halloumi. They also find space for tzatziki, and Glasgow salad - a scattering of chips. Unwrap, divide and hoover up. Halloumi fries are a conspicuous and popular signature dish. There's an express lunch menu Monday to Friday. The original Halloumi restaurant is on Hope Street.

Best Dish: **Swordfish and Prawn Souvlaki (£7.90)**

HANOI BIKE SHOP

8 Ruthven Ln, G12 9BG / 0141 334 7165 / hanoibikeshop.co.uk

It hits you right in the face when you walk in. A riot of exotic smells and colours. This was once the original home of The Ubiquitous Chip, back in the day. Now, Hanoi Bike Shop is well established as Glasgow's original Vietnamese hotspot. Dishes are conveyed from the kitchen speedily. We visit for crispy fried sea bass and pho bo marrow bone broth with beef fillet, brisket and slow cooked ox cheek. They make their own tofu from scratch here, which we enjoy served with roasted peanut, coconut and coriander. Street food options include salt and chilli squid or kimchi spring rolls. A tinge of West End gentility mixes surprisingly well with the casual aesthetic of a Southeast Asian roadside cafe.

Best Dish: **Chilli Pork Belly and Tofu (£12.95)**

THE HEBRIDEAN

333 Great Western Rd / 0141 339 3701 / the-hebridean.co.uk

Chef Nico Simeone travelled with his Exccutive Chef Andy Temple to the Outer Hebrides. The original intention was to gather ideas and devise a tasting menu for the Six by Nico concept. The brief visit inspired an entirely different idea. They returned and decided to bring a taste of the Western Isles to Great Western Road. The Hebridean was born over summer 2019. Charles MacLeod Stornoway black pudding, Uig Lodge smoked salmon, Hebridean wildfood seaweed and fresh shellfish caught from the Sound of Harris waters provide the building blocks for the menu. Order Tobermory Isle of Mull gin at the bar, and relax amidst Harris Tweed interiors. A neighbourhood gastropub that allows you to island-hop from your local. Epic Sunday roast menu.

Best Dish: **Fearann Eilean Iarmain Venison (£27)**

THE HUG AND PINT

171 Great Western Rd, G4 9AW / 0141 331 1901 / thehugandpint.com

The name comes from an Arab Strap song. Aidan Moffat from the band designed the logo. They won the Glasgow Chilli Cook-off with a pumpkin chilli - beating nine other bars and their assorted carnivorous versions in the public vote. Expect an accomplished, modern take on plant-based cooking, where Asian influences define the daily-changing menu and all manner of roasting, browning, slicing and garnishing is utilised to add umami and texture to the food. The mushroom and cashew curry is a great example: coconut milk providing a base from which a chilli-flake heat slowly rises and the ingredients crunch and slurp around sticky rice. Also a live music venue for left-field and alternative acts, and bar that buzzes along every night with a hip demeanour.

Best Dish: **Jackfruit Curry (£6.20)**

HUTCHESONS CITY GRILL

158 Ingram St, G1 1E J / 0141 552 4050 / hutchesonsglasgow.com

On every visit, we notice something different. A detail on the stained glass windows or those glorious high ceilings. Hutchesons is a stylish urban hangout with one of the most impressive dining rooms in the city. The building dates back to 1802 and was rescued from obscurity when it was transformed into a three floor restaurant. You'll find a menu that skillfully draws together the twin themes of seafood and steaks. The house steak cuts are hung and dry-aged for 28-35 days and the standard options are a fillet, sirloin, rib eye or D-rump which you can top with garlic prawns or half lobster tail and a sauce. Louise and James Rusk have created a modern classic, which gives this historic Merchant City building a new sense of purpose.

Best Dish: **Roast Shetland Monkfish Tail (£25)**

KA KA LOK

175 St George's Rd, G3 6JD / 0141 353 6528

Glasgow is not short of Chinese restaurants. If you are in search of a real taste experience, beyond the usual fried rice or sweet and sour sauce, those in the know come to Ka Ka Lok. There are two very long menus, one in English and one in Chinese. Both feature authentic preparations of popular dishes, but the Chinese version of the menu includes lots of red chillies and some ingredients that may raise an eyebrow. Be bold and dive in at the deep end of Chinese cuisine. Or look for upmarket specials like lobster with ginger and spring onion. Incidentally, the staff are that brilliant mix of attentive yet discreet, covertly keeping an eye on you to make sure you're not wanting for water, left with plates on the table for too long or reading your menu upside down.

Best Dish: Duck Kung Po (£10.95)

KELVINGROVE CAFÉ

1161 Argyle St, G3 8TB / 0141 221 8988 / kelvingrovecafe.com

Keeping the citizens of Finnieston well nourished and supplied with small-batch whiskies or robust craft ales is now one of the main functions of Argyle Street. Go to the Kelvingrove Café. It was a genteel ice cream parlour long ago, before the building was abandoned, only to gain a new lease of life as a bar and bistro six years ago. The interior features stripped-down bare brickwork and dark wood. On a Friday and Saturday night the neat downstairs bar is a popular venue for a chat and a meticulously put together cocktail. We are fans of the extensive brunch menu - order ham and eggs with Stornoway black pudding and crispy potatoes. The Kelvingrove Café was named the country's Most Stylish Bar at the Scottish Style Awards. It wears the title well.

Best Dish: Beef Goulash with Dumplings (£14)

KIMCHI CULT

14 Chancellor St, G11 5RQ / 0141 258 8081 / kimchicult.com

There are three things you need to try at Kimchi Cult. The kimchi itself, which is fiery and peppery. It is to be found on the burgers, the fries, and sometimes muddled into a quirky mac 'n' cheese special. Also, order some form of slow roasted animal - be it the remarkably juicy pork shoulder, or the bulgogi brisket with sesame and the aforementioned kimchi cutting through the dense, meaty shreds. You're not done yet. Ask for a portion of the fried chicken: twice-cooked so the brown meat within is loaded with moistness and flavour but the skin is a glossy, candy-crunch combination of sweet, savoury and sticky. Bibimbap and bao complete a formidable arsenal of Korean favourites. There's a lo-fi, street food aesthetic. A cool wee cafe serving a cheap, smashable munch.

Best Dish: Kimchi Burger (£7.50)

KOTHEL

300 Crow Rd, G11 7HS / 0141 258 4799 / fb.com/kothel300

A coffee shop and deli with a touch of the Mediterranean, Kothel opened on the bustling Crow Road in 2015 and serves a range of soups, salads, sandwiches and an extensive selection of homemade cakes, biscuits and sweet treats plus excellent coffee. The interior is eclectic to say the least, but the mix and match chairs and bric a brac add to the homely feel and character of the distinctive café. It's a busy spot, especially on weekend mornings, when you can enjoy brunch at close quarters to your neighbouring tables. Outdoor seating under the awing is ideal for those with dogs or anyone wanting to watch the world pass by on the Crow Road without being distracted by the weather. Kothel has expanded with cafes opening in Bearsden and on Great Western Road.

Best Dish: **Moussaka (£6.95)**

KURDISH STREET FOOD

12-14 Allison St, G42 8NN / 0141 423 7272

Kurdish Street Food have a reputation that goes far beyond their wee shop at the Pollokshaws Road end of Allison Street. They take kebabs seriously - minced lamb prepared with garlic, chillies and aubergines, cooked slowly over charcoal, served with salad and wrapped in naan bread. Ask them to wrap you up a satisfying version of Middle Eastern staple shawarma. Notice the mammoth size and myriad flavours in each mouthful. It's a rare eatery that you would visit to fuel your journey home after a big night out, then happily return to in the cold light of day for more sober dining to go. They do a roaring late trade but the place is equally as busy at lunchtime and dinner. Favourite starters include baba ganoush and falafel.

Best Dish: **Kurdish Kebab (£6.50)**

LA FIORENTINA

1 Paisley Rd West, G51 1LE / 0141 258 8081 / la-fiorentina.com

Serving pasta and wine since 1989, La Fiorentina sits at the top table of Paisley Road West and Kinning Park eateries. This old master keeps the locals happy with it's Tuscan-esque archways, the right level of pomp and ceremony, and those classic Italian dishes that Glaswegians have assumed as their own. So your bruschetta is there and arancini and Bolognese sauces are all on show. The rosé veal is well-priced and happily on the right side of medium rare within its breadcrumb coating. Pasta has that additional bit of thickness and bite that separates the decent stuff from the great stuff. Garlic and basil, San Marzano tomatoes - they all pop up and do their thing with confident, big-flavoured gusto.

Best Dish: **Penne Amatriciana (£9.95)**

LA LANTERNA

447 Gt Western Rd, G12 8HH / 0141 334 0686 / lalanternawestend.co.uk

Luca Conreno, the charismatic Head Chef at La Lanterna, brings flavours imported straight from Italy, to his Glasgow restaurants. Pasta tossed with bacon and garlic, finished with egg, parmesan and cream - the best version of carbonara in the city. Linguine with scallops, king prawns, monkfish and mussels. King prawns cooked in lemon juice, white wine and sweet chilli served on garlic bread. It's a gastronomic tour of regional cuisine, all from the comfort of your table on Hope Street or Great Western Road. An impeccable host, he is a passionate advocate for authentic Italian cuisine. A night out in La Lanterna is a joyful experience. Part of the local food story since 1970. Peter Mullan, Kevin Bridges, Johnny Logan and actor Chris Pine are fans.

Best Dish: Pennette alla Barese (£12.95)

LAGOM KITCHEN

76 Victoria Rd, G42 7AA / 0141 237 1940

Lagom is a quirky Scandinavian food concept, a close relative to the bang-on-trend hygge movement. It literally means "just the right amount". A slow-and-steady approach to sensible eating. What that translates to in Glasgow is a welcoming breakfast, brunch, lunch, cake and coffee place. Order plump pancakes wth caramelised peach, amaretto cream, white chocolate ganache, raspberry sauce and amaretti biscuit crumb. Or the hangover destroying Cubano sandwich of slow cooked pork, roast ham, pickles, Swiss cheese and mustard mayo if it is on the specials board. No wonder they are always so busy. Lagom Kitchen also plays host to regular pop-up supper club events. And knitting workshops.

Best Dish: **Corn Fritters and Pork Belly (£9)**

LE PETIT COCHON

9 Radnor St, G3 7UA / 0141 357 1666 / lepetitcochon.co.uk

Sitting on the edge of Kelvingrove Park, Le Petit Cochon is an independently owned neighbourhood wine bar and bistro that has stormed its way into the affections of locals. They serve food all day, seven days a week in a cosy, fairy-lit dining room. The bistro transforms local produce and imported treats into strong, seasonal dishes - small plates, main courses and sharing plates. The extensive wine list features a range of options from Europe, with more wines by the glass than anywhere in Glasgow, to go with your charcuterie and cheese. The staff will happily chat you through what goes with your meal. At brunch, order a buttery croissant with bacon, Gruyère and a fried egg for a suitably continental start to the day.

Best Dish: **Confit Duck Leg, Celeriac Purée (£16)**

LEIPER'S ATTIC

93-95 Hyndland St, G11 5PU / 0141 357 5825 / leipersattic.com

Amidst imposing West End red sandstone terraces, meandering lanes and pockets of park greenery, Leiper's Attic has carved out a reputation for serving a fine selection of wild game, wild fish and in-house dry aged beef dishes. You'll find them at the top of a winding staircase in Cottiers, the popular theatre and wedding venue created when the Four Acres Charitable Trust set about preserving the Dowanhill Church more than 20 years ago. Leiper's Attic's self-defined mission is to showcase the best of Scotland's larder. All the beef served from the grill is aged in house for 28 days. Look for prize cuts from herds in Perthshire or Renfrewshire. Named after William Leiper, who designed this church and the facade of Templeton's Carpet Factory on Glasgow Green.

Best Dish: **Fillet Steak (£30)**

LYCHEE ORIENTAL

59 Mitchell St, G1 3LN / 0141 248 2240 / lycheeoriental.co.uk

Jimmy Lee is the owner and head chef of Glasgow's leading Cantonese restaurant, Lychee Oriental on Mitchell Street. His enthusiasm for Asian food and culinary flair has led to a clutch of award wins, including Scottish Personality Chef of the Year at the 2018 Food & Drink Awards and Best Asian Restaurant in Scotland at the Entertainment Awards. He started work in his dad's takeaway when he was 16 years old and has seldom been far from a kitchen since. Lychee Oriental chefs transform Scottish ingredients with Chinese cooking techniques, sourcing game or fish to incorporate them into traditional dishes, like wok fried Scottish mussels with chillies and black beans or steamed scallops with garlic, ginger and spring onion.

Best Dish: **Roast Duck With Lychees in Plum Sauce (£16.50)**

MACKINTOSH AT THE WILLOW

215 Sauchiehall St, G2 3EX / 0141 204 1903 / mackintoshatthewillow.com

The original Willow Tea Rooms building on Sauchiehall Street was reopened to celebrate the 150th anniversary of the birth of its designer Charles Rennie Mackintosh. The 200-seat restaurant and tea rooms was returned to its intended form by a painstaking £10 million restoration. The building, which first opened in 1903, is the only one where Mackintosh had total control over the architecture and interior decorations, including the design of furniture, and cutlery. Enjoy a meaty full Scottish breakfast in the morning. Admire the elegant, bright salon as you enjoy afternoon tea with finger sandwiches, plain and fruit scones with clotted cream and preserves alongside a selection of homemade cakes.

Best Dish: Classic Afternoon Tea (£19.03)

MESA

567 Duke St, G31 1PY / 0141 237 2040 / instagram.com/mesa_glasgow

Cafe Strange Brew owner Laurie MacMillan and fellow chef Andrea Bartolini opened Mesa on Duke Street earlier this year for all-day brunch. A compact, bright space with bare stone walls adorned with prints, including an eye-catching one of Tom Waits. There are design cues from its Southside sister cafe, but Mesa has already established its own identity in the East End. They are ready for visitors, 9-5pm, Tuesday to Sunday. Let's cut straight to the menu. Thick chunks of sourdough. Slabs of halloumi. Expertly poached eggs. Pancakes layered with fruits These are some of the essential building blocks of the dishes that have a starring role on weekend Instagram feeds. For a big breakfast, we usually order the hot lamb red shakshuka two egg skillet.

Best Dish: **Pancakes, Maple, Bacon and Blueberries (£7)**

MOTHER INDIA

28 Westminster Terrace, G3 7RU / 0141 221 1663 / motherindia.co.uk

Mother India opened in 1996, with Mother India's Café, pioneering Indian tapas and small plates, opening next door in 2004. The original idea was simple – serve authentic Indian home cooking at affordable prices. This restaurant has been the high mark for Glasgow curries ever since. Dining is split over three floors – a moodily lit basement, a cosy ground floor dining room and bar, which includes Bungalow Café, an ice cream parlour that also serves tea, coffee and desserts, and a spacious, candle-lit third floor which has antique furniture, wood panelling and dark red walls. Portions are generous. Stand-out dishes include ginger crab and prawn dosa, haddock oven baked with punjabi spices and lamb raan sharer.

Best Dish: Black Daal (£8)

MUSSEL INN

157 Hope St, G2 2UQ / 0141 572 1405 / mussel-inn.com

Award-winning Scottish seafood restaurant Mussel Inn was founded 20 years ago by a mussel farmer and a scallop farmer who decided to buck the trend of Scottish shellfish being immediately exported to the continent by making it available in their own restaurant. Known for its passion for locally sourced fresh seafood, providing excellent value for money with a quick and friendly service, Mussel Inn is headed by Swedish father and son team Janne and Matt Johansson. While mussels remain a staple of its menu, it offers a broader selection of dishes. Their sustainably cultivated oysters, nurtured in the cold sea lochs of the west coast, grow more slowly than those from warmer waters, providing a remarkable depth of taste.

Best Dish: **White Wine and Shallot Mussels (£15.60)**

NAKODAR

13 Annfield Pl, G31 2XQ / 0141 556 4430 / nakodargrill.com

It's a brave soul who tells someone from Dennistoun that their very own Nakodar isn't the best Indian restaurant in Glasgow. We are lucky to have a particularly high standard of Mughal-influenced Indian cuisine across the city and Nakodar is a fine case-in-point. A comfortable neighbourhood vibe, but with a kitchen that knows how to handle those big, bombastic flavours. Sauces are cooked down and thick, with a dry, meaty heat, and anything from the tandoor is worth a punt, from lamb chops to salmon to a baby masala chicken. Marinades, cooking times, temperatures - dishes feel like they've been made with a mastery of all those sorts of components. Friendly service and some cracking haggis pakora, too.

Best Dish: Nakodari Lamb (£11.95)

NANIKA

72 Victoria Rd, G42 7AA / 07383 716676/ nanika2.neocities.org

Justin Valmassoi "bounced all over the place" - Detroit, Grand Rapids, Philadelphia, Chicago, Seattle - before landing in Glasgow, six years ago. He took over a space on Victoria Road and Nanika was born. "I dated a Vietnamese girl for two years, and her family basically fed me all kinds of food that I had never remotely experienced. That's the flavours that I gravitate towards. Southeast Asian". Nanika is small. There's space for Justin in the kitchen, a server and 13 customers. On the menu, there's 25-30 items with rotating specials. The equipment and logistics of the kitchen dictates what they can make. Diners can see what's going on in the kitchen and are close enough to be able to shout some encouragement. Go for spicy noodle soups, Saigon salad, fried tofu, pillowy steamed buns, prawn tempura, chicken katsu, salmon ponzu bowls or house kimchi. New menu items are constantly appearing and disappearing. To keep things interesting, Justin hits up the Asian markets in the north of the city looking for "weird pickles and unusual food packs. If I can't read the label, I'm buying it and I'll figure out what to do with it." It's fast street food. Dishes are colourful and creative. Bring your own bottle with a £2.50 corkage charge. That's per person, not per bottle. Open for dinner 5pm-10pm Wednesday-Sunday. They operate a text-based queue system during busy periods. Come sit close to someone you don't know, drink oolong tea and order a spicy dish.

Best Dish: Sichuan Noodles (£8)

NON VIET

536 Sauchiehall St, G2 3LX / 0141 332 2975 / nonviet.co.uk

Pho, the classic Vietnamese fragrant homemade broth, is ideal comfort food for the Glasgow climate. You'll find the city's best example of the dish on Sauchiehall Street. Garnished with spring onion and coriander, served with beanspouts, lemon and fresh chopped chili. Top with fried tofu, shredded chicken or cooked and rare beef. It's good for what ails you. Non Viet is casual dining with plenty of room for groups to share a selection of dishes. Ask questions if you don't understand any of the ingredients and be adventurous with your choices. For dessert, it's the dried ice cream with a sprinkle of condensed milk and crush peanut, or mango spring roll with creamy coconut sauce for us. Sister restaurant Non Viet Hai is on Great Western Road.

Best Dish: **Hue Spicy Noodle Soup (£11.50)**

NUMBER 16

16 Byres Rd, G11 5JY / 0141 339 2544 / number16.co.uk

A cosy, well-established and much loved neighbourhood favourite. Number 16 is known for its modern twist on traditional Scottish cooking. Their set lunch menu is some of the best value you will find on Byres Road, with two impressive courses for £18 and three courses for £21. Dishes include celeriac and apple soup, wild venison ragu with fresh tagliatelle and greengage, nectarine and white peach crumble. Each plate is imacculatlely presented, a feast for the senses prepared by the talented, tight-knit team led by owner Joel Pomfret. A compact space with a mezzanine, it's a restaurant you can count on, regularly receiving positive reviews. Named Best Local Restaurant in Scotland by The Good Food Guide.

Best Dish: Roasted Haunch of Perthshire Venison (£21)

OLD SALTY'S

337 Byres Rd, G12 8UQ / 0141 378 6592 / oldsaltys.co.uk

This high-end chippy and cafe is back on Byres Road, reestablished after a fire that gutted the premises. Like a phoenix rising from the flames, they returned after nine-months, sporting a new look and serving up a steady supply of classic fish suppers. Vegan and gluten-free options are available. Interesting furniture and plusher fixtures and fittings than you might expect. Eye up items from the menu, bathed in light in the stainless steel cabinet. The smell of salt and vinegar hangs in the air. Service starts early with cooked breakfasts popular at weekends. Local students pour in at lunchtime for haggis, smoked sausage, hake, cod and haddock. Tip: They serve the best macaroni pie in the city.

Best Dish: Haddock Fish Supper (£10.95)

ONE DEVONSHIRE GARDENS

1 Devonshire Gdns, G1 / 0141 378 0385 / hotelduvin.com

Gary Townsend is an ambitious chef with over 16 years of experience in some of the country's top kitchens including The Kitchin, and Restaurant Martin Wishart, where he worked as a sous chef during the time the restaurant was awarded a Michelin Star back in 2011. If Glasgow has any reputation as a city that takes cooking seriously, then that stature is built on the bedrock of places like One Devonshire Gardens. This is an address that means something, a byword for fine dining and discreet hospitality. An evening here is impressive. Expect quality produce including Loch Fyne scallop, Goosnargh duck and Highland deer on the menu. Seasonal tasting menus with wine flights are recommended.

Best Dish: John Dory With Violet Artichokes (£29)

ÒRAN MÓR

Top of Byres Rd, G12 8QX / 0141 357 6200 / oran-mor.co.uk

More than a great bar, they say. Òran Mór, within the stately surroundings of what was Kelvinside Parish Church, with its tall Gothic spire, was saved from being turned into luxury flats by Colin Beattie. He had a higher purpose in mind, a place where arts and culture could sit alongside food and drink. A Play, A Pie and a Pint is their most famous performance series, one that produces the most new-writing of any theatre in the UK. It's launched careers and memorable lunchtimes. Tucked away in what was the old manse, The Brasserie at Òran Mór boasts Art Nouveau inspired prints and generous portions of game, wild mushrooms, hake and salmon. The John Muir Room menu has bar bites like steak pie, moules frites or haggis bonbons.

Best Dish: **Supreme of Chicken (£16.95)**

PAESANO PIZZA

94 Miller St, G1 1DT / 0141 258 5565 / paesanopizza.co.uk

A legend in its own lunchtime. Glasgow's most popular pizza. What's the story with the clamour for seats at their hip city centre restaurant and Great Western Road joint? Well, Glasgow has spent the last couple of years realising pizza does not have to be a plate of disappointing round stodge. Nothing against our local deep fried version, but it turns out that the Italians in Naples got it right first time round. Paesano has nailed the cool, casual dining aesthetic. Then there's the pizza itself. Straight out of wood-fired ovens that provide an intense heat of 500 degrees Celsius to convert a pizza base into a pliable, light and tasty platform for all kinds of fresh toppings and transform the cheese into a creamy delight. Opening new city centre pasta place, Sugo, for 2020.

Best Dish: Spianata Spicy Salami, Mozzarella Pizza (£8)

PARTICK DUCK CLUB

27 Hyndland St, G11 5QF / 0141 334 9909 / partickduckclub.co.uk

Partick Duck Club is exactly the type of comfortable and accomplished restaurant everyone would like to have at the end of their street. Expect a stylish, bijou dining room and assured cooking. We like the wee tartan clad booths and would linger awhile at the small bar near the kitchen. Mostly, we like their straightforward approach to creating dishes from excellent Scottish produce and providing cheerful hospitality all week. It's the sort of place that is habit forming. You will want to return regularly. The talented duo in charge, Ross McDonald and Greig Hutcheson, worked together in restaurants for almost twenty years, before setting out on their own, here, in 2017. The focus is on quality comfort food and Partick Duck Club is really establishing its reputation on this residential corner of Hyndland Street. Duck does feature prominently on the menu here but doesn't dominate.For mains, try the shredded bbq duck leg with pomegranate mayo, coriander and pickled cabbage on a brioche bun. Roast squash, smoked haddock, Barra monkfish scampi or crispy pork if you are not here to tuck into duck. The all-day brunch and breakfast menu is another reason to visit. Look for the shakshuka baked eggs, green harissa and toasted sourdough from Freedom Bakery, or the innovative, rich combination of 24 hour beef shin and duck egg Benedict. Whatever time of day you visit, always order the duck fat fries topped with truffle mayo, Parmesan and black pepper. Fit to grace any Glasgow table.

Best Dish: 12-Hour Duck Leg and Crispy Duck Egg (£16.75)

PHILLIE'S OF SHAWLANDS

1179 Pollokshaws Rd, G41 3YH / 0141 616 6555 / philliesbar.co.uk

They opened the first bar in the country to pay the living wage to all staff and created a community hub with soul on Duke Street with Redmond's. For their next trick, brothers Conor and Luke Miskimmin founded another neighbourhood venue, this time in Shawlands, where they both live. At weekends, locals bring records to play on the bar turntables or enjoy the venue's own extensive vinyl collection, whilst sipping pints from Magic Rock, Cromarty or Fallen Brewing. Order impressive sourdough stone baked pizzas with toppings like parma ham, chorizo, aubergine or artichokes. There's always bao buns on the menu, our favourite filling is spiced halloumi with avocado and pickled cabbage. "A great place to be social" says Conor.

Best Dish: **Roasted Sweet Potato and Kale Salad (£9.50)**

PORTER & RYE

1131 Argyle St, G3 8ND / 0141 572 1212 / porterandrye.com

Porter & Rye's dry-aged beef is delivered daily by Tom Rodgers Butchers of
Byres Road. It's all sourced from the Brown family at Gaindykehead Farm of
Airdrie. They've been working closely with the farm since the doors opened
on Argyle Street in 2014. You'll see a range of popular and lesser known cuts
of steak, sausages and cured meats in the display fridge. Take your pick. If the
bovine bounty doesn't catch your eye, Porter & Rye also serves fish dishes and
a selection of vegetarian plates, often featuring locally foraged ingredients.
They mix up some inventive cocktails at the bar - ask for a Caribbean Affogato
after dinner. Sunday roast is a glorious slow-cooked beef brisket, bavette steak
served with Yorkshire pudding and beef dripping roasties.

Best Dish: Chateaubriand cut for two (£75)

RAMEN DAYO

31 Ashton Ln, G12 8SJ / 0141 334 9095 / ramendayo.com

Like many of the the more interesting new arrivals on the Glasgow food scene, Ramen Dayo - it means "This is Ramen" - started as a pop-up, making an eye-catching debut by taking over a covered lane in Gordon Street and converted it into a scene from a Tokyo back-alley, complete with lanterns, a Yatai cart and Japanese bar snacks. They are now thriving on Ashton Lane. Hearty bowls of ramen, prepared from scratch with variations on a rich, creamy pork broth with springy noodles, chashu pork belly, marinated kirkurage mushrooms, nori seaweed, egg and spring onions. The New York Times was impressed. There's also gyoza dumplings. imported sake, turntables and curated playlists. Founder Paul Beveridge was inspired by 12 years living in Japan.

Best Dish: **New Wave Tokyo Style Ramen (£8.90)**

RANJIT'S KITCHEN

607 Pollokshaws Rd, G41 2QG / 0141 423 8222 / ranjitskitchen.com

Ranjit Kaur is a Sikh woman from the village of Jandiala in the Jalandhar district of the Panjab, the north west of India. She has lived in Glasgow since 1990 and her family-run deli is a Southside favourite. They serve authentic, homemade food "precisely the way it is eaten in every Panjabi household across the world". The vegetarian dishes, including all curries, are made fresh every day from whatever ingredients are available at local fruit and veg shops. Always order Ranjit's special pakora, made with a mix of cauliflower, spinach, onions, potatoes and spices in gramflour batter served with chutney. The desserts - which include barfi, a smooth sweet made with ground almonds, milk, sugar and cream - are a real treat.

Best Dish: **Daal of the Day (£3.95)**

RED ONION

257 West Campbell St, G2 4TT / 0141 221 6000 / red-onion.co.uk

John Quigley's culinary career started off in London's West End where he quickly established his reputation for excellent casual gourmet dining. He then took the chance to tour the world as a private chef to rock stars and celebrities, including Bryan Adams, Tina Turner and Guns N' Roses, being asked to roast reindeer on a spit outside a venue in Sweden on the whim of a guitarist. After returning to Glasgow, John and his wife Gillian, decided to set out on their own, with smart city centre brasserie Red Onion opening its doors in 2005. The pre-theatre menu is popular with two courses for £15.50 and three courses for £17.65, including dishes like goats cheese salad, chargrilled lemon chicken and Arran smoked cheddar with fruit chutney and crackers.

Best Dish: **Quigley's Red Ale Braised Brisket (£16.50)**

ROASTIT BUBBLY JOCKS

450 Dumbarton Rd, G11 6SE / 0141 339 3355 / roastitbubblyjocks.com

During the day, the delightfully named Roastit Bubbly Jocks is every inch
the classic Glasgow cafe. We are all pre-programmed to find these types of
places when out for a wander. Somewhere for a satisfying pause, the forensic
examination of local gossip, a bit of comfort food and a strong pot of tea.
Quirkily dressed in paintings and retro ornaments, it's an interesting room.
Spot the picture of Stanley Baxter in the corner. In the evening there's more
of a buzzy bistro vibe. Things move up a gear with the seasonal a la carte
menu. It's packed with big-time courses like Argyll venison, sweet potato
dauphinouse, butternut and red cabbage or Isle of Lewis lamb with parmentier
potato and celeriac. A Partick eatery with a lot of personality.

Best Dish: **Chicken and Black Pudding (£15.95)**

THE RUM SHACK

657 Pollokshaws Road, G41 2AB / 0141 237 4432 / rumshackglasgow.com

The Rum Shack hasn't single-handedly made the Southside hip again, but it definitely gave things a nudge in that direction. The evening crowd is sprinkled with boho creatives, people in bands and people who look like they are in bands. It's also pretty much the only out-and-out Caribbean bar and restaurant in town, with made-to-order dishes that pack a vibrant punch. As expected, there's jerk chicken. But there's also chicken brown down - three bits of the good stuff, on the bone, in a sticky and satisfyingly dark sauce of meaty depth balanced with brown sugar sweetness, served with a wedge of macaroni bake and boiled greens. Rum Shack has that little bit of random magic. A local bar in a palette of red, green and yellow with over 100 rums ready for you.

Best Dish: Jerk Fish and Chips (£9.50)

SARAMAGO

350 Sauchiehall St, G2 3JD / 0141 352 4920 / media.cca-glasgow.com

Serving colourful, wholesome food every day – including home-baked bread and cakes each morning – Saramago is one of the city's top food places for vegetarians and vegans. The team work with ethical suppliers, with the menu being shaped by the best ingredients available on the day. Located within the Centre for Contemporary Arts in a repurposed courtyard complete with colourful festoon lights. The café also serves a range of beers, ciders, wines and juices, which can be enjoyed inside the upstairs bar or on the outdoor terrace. We like their sourdough pizza topped with cashew parmesan and rocket Artichokes, olives, kale and chilli on tomato sugo. Saramago attracts a cultured crowd, regularly hosting guest DJs, exhibitions and small gigs.

Best Dish: **Thai Green Curry With Sweet Potato (£10.50)**

SHAWARMA KING

113 King St, G1 5RB/ 0141 258 1870

Tony Stark finished an Avengers movie saying: "Have you ever had shawarma? I don't know what it is but I want to try it". It's a question for the ages. A thought that might drift through your mind after a few happy pints in the Merchant City. It's at that point you might toddle down the road to Shawarma King for the first time. They will introduce you the Levantine delights of boneless lamb, chicken or beef, marinated in a spice blend, layered onto a giant spit and slowly roasted at a high temperature. Someone will quickly shave off mounds of the meat and serve with rice and salad or pile it into a wrap of freshly baked naan bread then add pickles, salad and homemade garlic and chilli sauce. You will leave very happy and content.

Best Dish: **Large Shawarma Kebab (£5.99)**

THE SINGL-END

263 Renfrew St, G3 6TT / 0141 353 1277 / thesingl-end.co.uk

The Singl-End is one of our favourite ways to start the day. The café and bakehouse's menu is a mix of the unusual and the familiar, spiked with superfood ingredients like Camargue rice and quinoa, nuts, citrus fruits and spices. Book a table with friends and family. Walk up Garnethill and enter the open dining room, full of chat and positivity. There's a bit of an Italian influence in the menu. You'll find excellent vegan and vegetarian options. We order the meaty baked eggs, oven baked in a casserole of homemade pork and fennel sausage, cannellini beans, tomato and chilli. It's morning comfort food as an art form, served in an oversized hot skillet. To be enjoyed with tea, smoothies or wine, and followed by something from the cake table.

Best Dish: **Meaty Baked Eggs With Mozzarella (£1250)**

THE SPANISH BUTCHER

80 Miller St, G1 1DT / 0141 406 9880 / spanishbutcher.com

The Spanish Butcher has carved out a stellar reputation serving the finest grades of Galician Beef, premium Iberico Jamon and seafood infused with Spanish and Mediterranean flavours. Hollywood actor Will Ferrell was a recent diner and ordered second helpings of the Manchego mac n cheese with puffed paprika pork skin. Vegetarian options include the cauliflower steak with potatoes a la pobre, caperberries, piquillo peppers and salsa verde. The chic interior takes inspiration from New York's dining scene. Order an espresso martini at the bar after dinner. In 2018, The Spanish Butcher was the first Scottish restaurant to be nominated in the Best Restaurant in the UK category at the GQ Food & Drinks Awards.

Best Dish: **Abanico Iberico de Bellota (£19)**

STRAVAIGIN

28 Gibson St, G12 8NX / 0141 334 2665 / stravaigin.co.uk

Regular customers can't remember a time before Stravaigin, a Gibson Street favourite since the mid-90s. It led the way for eateries serving local produce with global culinary influences. A model that paved the way for many other bistros that followed. It continues to raise our expectations. The menu segues through mealtimes, starting with brunchy riffs on stalwarts like buckwheat and peanut pancakes or a chipotle scrambled duck egg. At lunchtime there's an emphasis on sharing plates. In the evening, cuisines combine: North Sea cod is given a Sri Lankan marinade and finished with some Mediterranean-esque raita and cashews. Dishes have character. Always ask about the specials. Tip: Stravaigin has a 1am licence and a long wine list.

Best Dish: **Shetland Hake, Charred Corn, Haricot Bean Salsa (£18)**

TIFFNEY'S STEAKHOUSE

61 Otago St, G12 8PQ / 0141 328 9557 / tiffneys.co.uk

Tiffney's Steakhouse is housed in what was once a car showroom, wedged in amongst the quaint tenement buildings of Otago Street. Now it is where they show off their prize butcher cuts. Bare brick walls, comfy seats, a collection of tables built to support the carving of formidable steaks. A 500g tomahawk! A 1kg porterhouse T-bone to share! The type of plates that always get a reaction when they appear, even when you know what's coming. When you come to Tiffney's you are shopping at the top end of Scotch beef, reared in the North East of Scotland and dry aged on the bone for a minimum of 70 days. Add some prawns or haggis and find space at the table for sides of honey roasted chantenay carrots and parsnips or sauteed garlic mushrooms.

Best Dish: **Extra Matured Fillet Steak (£19/100g)**

TOPOLABAMBA

89 St Vincent St, G2 5TF/ 0141 248 9359/ topolabamba.com

The large open dining room may look a bit like every other generic high street Mexican joint, but this is the real deal. They take inspiration from the four main regions of Mexico: Oaxaca, Chiapas, Chihuahua and their namesake, Topolabamba. It's street food for sharing. Portion size varies but they always say two or three dishes per person should do. Excellent vegetarian and gluten free options. Powerful flavours and an uptempo atmosphere. There's an express lunch menu if you are in a hurry. On our last visit we enjoyed barbacoa beef and crumbly cheese tacos, smoked chorizo quesadillas, seriously hot habenero chicken wings, and green peppers stuffed with potato and feta, all washed down by a couple of rounds of frozen mango margaritas. Muy bien.

Best Dish: Carne Asada Steak Tacos (£6.50)

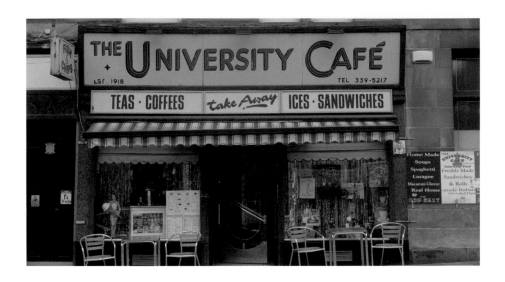

UNIVERSITY CAFÉ

87 Byres Rd, G11 5HN / 0141 339 5217

A living part of the local food story is 101 years old. The University Café is a throwback to the first proliferation of ice cream parlours across the city. It's enduring appeal is down to an idiosyncratic family-friendly fusion of Italian and Glaswegian influences, held together in a tiny Art Deco room with slim wood-lined booths and bedecked in kitschy nostalgia. Students depend on their hangover crushing meals like pie, beans and chips or macaroni and chips. They sell a lot of chips. Someday you may need their comforting version of the Glasgow Diet. Owner Carlo Verrecchia makes ice cream to an old family recipe that has been passed down through the generations. It's smooth and super-sweet, a reminder of a carefree past, before Irn Bru changed.

Best Dish: **Pie and Chips (£3.70)**

URBAN BAR AND BRASSERIE

25 St Vincent Pl, G1 2DT / 0141 248 5636 / urbanbrasserie.co.uk

Right in the centre of town, Urban is smart and traditional, a spacious brasserie with attentive staff, just off a dark wood bar with more casual seating. Modern art, booths, high ceilings, crisp white linen tableclothes and a welcome sense of occasion. Head Chef John Paul Lappin heads up the kitchen, serving a menu dominated by classic dishes, given a bit of a Glasgow remix in some cases. The popular market menu features haggis bon bons, steak frites and pan fried bass. The laidback afternoon vibe gives way to a more buzzy atmosphere in the evening. On a Friday or Saturday night there's a piano player in the corner and cocktail bar staff are in demand - try a Ginger Rodgers: Wildcat Gin, sliced apple, lychee water and cucumber tonic. Brunch served seven days a week.

Best Dish: **Crab Linguine (£14.50)**

WEE LOCHAN

340 Crow Rd, G11 7HQ / 0141 338 6606 / an-lochan.com

In Broomhill, on Crow Road, Wee Lochan is a charming family-run restaurant that champions Scottish produce, served in its cosy, atmospheric dining room. Open for lunch, Monday to Saturday, 12-3pm and dinner, 5-10pm, with an all day Sunday roast available from 12-7pm. Wee Lochan has a simple neighbourhood cafe feel that belies the quality of its food and service. The menu varies daily depending on what comes in fresh from suppliers, but you can always count on there being a warming bowl of cullen skink, a range of fish dishes, an expertly made soufflé, as well as interesting vegetarian choices. Wee Lochan may be easy-going and understated, but it's a big hit with customers and food critics.

Best Dish: Twice-baked Mull Cheddar Soufflé (£7.50)

WEST ON THE GREEN

Templeton St, G40 1AW / 0141 550 0135 / westbeer.com/westonthegreen

The story of West Brewery is a belter. German Petra Wetzel is studying at Glasgow University. Her dad comes over to visit. They start talking about beer. Petra has a plan. She graduates and starts a micro-brewery in Glasgow Green's Templeton Building. A rollercoaster few years follow, but now West is firmly established as part of the city's craft beer scene. You'll get St Mungo, their flagship helles-style lager. all over town, but it's worth going to the source. Food here looks to both Germany and Scotland - haggis, neeps and tatties, and fish and chips are flanked by spaetzle and smoked bratwurst sausages, in a nicely fiery, properly sticky sauce with a dunt of cloves and a brisk dollop of sauerkraut. Their dog-friendly beer garden is one of the best in the city.

Best Dish: **Beer Glazed Brats (£11.50)**

THE WINGED OX

17 Bain St, G40 2JZ / 0141 552 8378 / stlukesglasgow.com

The Winged Ox is the food and drink side of the operation at ultra-hip East End venue St Luke's. The stage in the converted church is regularly graced by some of the biggest names on the music scene for gigs. Meanwhile, the kitchen is cooking up its own headliners on a daily basis. Some of our favourites are the brisket burger, fish finger sandwich or Calton kebabs – gourmet offerings with options like soulaki pork, Cajun chicken and Moroccan veg. Elsewhere on the menu, expect lots of American-tinged soul food with a bit of Glaswegian swagger. It's good, honest bar food, to be shared with friends between rounds of craft beer or bourbon cocktails. The kitchen is open until 9pm Sunday-Thursday, then until 10pm on Friday and Saturday. You can expect the occasional singer with a guitar as entertainment while you eat. The benches on the outside terrace are a suntrap during the summer and booths in the bar are regularly booked out at weekends so groups can enjoy burgers and beers. The building has been here for 200 years but it's only been a venue since 2015, after a refit from brothers Michael and Tony Woods. It's strength has been establishing The Winged Ox as an integral part of the community. You'll see all the family here for dinner. Passing leather--clad-rockers or tattooed indie kids are made to feel at home. They are a dog-friendly bar too, with a dedicated food menu for pets to enjoy. It's all an eclectic mix to match the varied menu.

Best Dish: Souvlaki Pork Wrap (£7)

WHERE THE MONKEY SLEEPS

340 Argyle St, G2 8LY / 0141 204 5260 / monkeysleeps.com

The best bagels in town, a minimalist design aesthetic, heavy metal inspired artwork and playlists. Popular bagels include the Witchfynder (chorizo, smoked cheese, chilli mayo). You will also find paninis like the Firewalker Deluxe (turkey, bacon, cheddar, chillies, hot sauce) and their own version of beans on toast. Get involved. Rodgers and MacSween's are meat suppliers not uncommonly mentioned on top restaurant menus. That they are proudly listed here is indicative of how seriously WTMS takes its ingredients. There is a rugged vibrancy to everything, with tarragon and lemon juice and balsamic vinegar all popping up to make lunchtime a bit more exciting, a bit more rock 'n' roll and distinctive. Warming stews in winter and strong coffee as standard.

Best Dish: **Meathammer Bagel (£5.90)**

YADGAR

148 Calder St, G42 7QP / 0141 424 3722

Go to Yadgar for a spice less ordinary. Cast your eyes over open trays of simple, Pakistani homecooking. Lamb with potatoes; chicken and spinach; chickpeas and tomatoes with vegetables. As unassuming a food place as they come, yet Southsiders swear by it, and with good reason. Chicken keema mince, served with potatoes and peas, is a comforting mix of dry, oily heat and juicy meat. Anyone who likes both curries, and stovies - or thinks they might - would be well advised to order a large plate. We like their samosas, made in-house with care. The result is just that little bit better than you get elsewhere - more airy, more flaky. If you're serious about the more authentic dining experiences in the city, then Yadgar is the one for you.

Best Dish: Shami Kebab (£1 per kebab)

BEST CAFES

Cake, Coffee and Quick Bites

CAKE BAR

401 Great Western Rd, G4 9HY / 0333 344 5415 / cakebaruk.com

Three Sisters Bake serve fresh, colourful, local food bursting with flavour. Their modern take on a country tearoom offers hearty dishes alongside a cavalcade of delightful sweet treats. Already established on the periphery of the city at Quarrier's Village and Killearn, they brought a new maverick offshoot to Great Western Road when Cake Bar opened in a blaze of colour over the summer. The takeaway and coffee cafe features their own distinctive bakes, ice cream, hot brownie sundaes, celebration cakes and a loaded pick 'n' mix counter. Get a slice of the good life.

YOUR COFFEE SHOP CHECKLIST

Gordon Street Coffee, 79 Gordon St, G1 3SQ
Small batch coffee roaster near Central Station

Primal Roast, 278 St Vincent St, G2 5RL
Clean eating, healthy food and coffee

Spitfire Espresso, 127 Candleriggs, G1 1NP
Friendly, independent coffee spot with all day breakfast

TANTRUM DOUGHNUTS

28 Gordon St, G1 3PU
0141 248 1552
tantrumdoughnuts.com

Glasgow is doughnuts daft. So, when Tantrum, the brainchild of husband and wife team Iain and Annika Baillie began making pop-up appearances at markets, they attracted a crowd. Then came a shop on Old Dumbarton Road, which opened in December 2015 and has become a firm favourite in the neighbourhood.

For their next trick, Tantrum rolled into the city centre, opening on Gordon Street, close to Central Station. Enter and you are greeted by an outlandish display of fun treats. Brioche doughnuts, hand-made in small batches, then smothered, filled or glazed with home-made custards, fondants, purées, compotes and jams. Their selection changes when new flavours become available from local suppliers. Our current favourite is crème brûlée.

PIECE

1056 Argyle St, G3 8LY
0141 221 7975
pieceglasgow.com

They've entertained and fed lunchtime crowds across the city while growing a successful local sandwich business, which now includes seven stores. Piece have always set out to make an impression, get the food right, and have fun. Signature sandwiches include the Cubano with slow roast pork, sliced roast ham, gouda cheese, gherkins, spinach, aioli and mustard.

Alongside their Argyle Street location, you will find Piece's enthusiastic staff on Waterloo Street, plus West Regent Street, Miller Street, The Whisky Bond building, Dawson Road and the Inovo Building on Albion Street. Ready to serve up something tasty to add cheer to your lunchtime.

KAF COFFEE

5 Hyndland St, G11 5QE
kafcoffee.co.uk

A cute speciality coffee and brunch
cafe that attracts a crowd with
unusual dishes, a friendly welcome
and benches outside when it's sunny.
Part of the Partick weekend tradition,
Kaf was cited by the New York Times
travel section as one of the places
making Glasgow a more interesting
destination for tourists. Locals are
equally as enthusiastic.

Look for Scandi plates of boiled egg,
crispy bacon, cheese, new potato,
houmous, sourdough, fruit and
granola yoghurt at weekends. Or
home-made babkha French toast
with pistachio frangipane, lemon
curd, whipped cream, nuts and
berries.

Their coffee offering includes an ever-
changing rotation of single origin
coffees on both espresso and filter.

COMET PIECES

150 Queen Margaret Dr, G20 8NY
0141 945 2135
cometpieces.co.uk

Bal Sandhu and Carla Jack fulfilled a
long-held ambition to open their own
cafe. The name is "inspired by the PS
Comet: a paddle steamer launched
on the Clyde in 1812 and which is
commemorated by way of a large
wall painting in the cafe". Clyde-built
still means something.

Visit for their out-of-this-world
signature rolls, brunches, cakes and
coffees and teas. Bread is supplied
by Freedom Bakery and their most
popular menu items are served in
Mortons rolls or baked in-house
wholemeal rolls.

Fillings like 24-hour marinated
shredded chicken thigh, Stornoway
black pudding, spring onions
and sriracha mayo make a big
impression.

BEST STREET FOOD
Markets and Meet-Ups Across the City

PLATFORM AT ARGYLE ST ARCHES
253 Argyle Street, G2 8DL / argylestarches.com/platform

Bringing some of Glasgow's best independent street food traders together every Friday, Saturday and Sunday within the city centre. Transforming the famous event space at Argyle Street Arches with big flavours, music, craft beer and family-friendly fun.

BIG FEED
249-325 Govan Rd, G51 2SE / fb.com/bigfeedgla

Growing local street food brands find a home in Govan. Organised in an indoor warehouse venue that plays host to new food concepts and local brewers.

DOCKYARD SOCIAL
95-107 Haugh Road, G3 8TY / dockyardsocial.com

A converted West End industrial warehouse, featuring ten passionate street food vendors, providing a social dining experience and global flavours.

BEST BARS
Get Your Glasgow Pub Food

BREL
37-43 Ashton Lane, G12 8SJ / 0141 342 4966 / brelbar.com

When we think of Brel we think of pints in the front bar, lunch upstairs, or maybe sitting outside on the hill in the garden with a DJ playing whenever there is a glimmer of sunshine. It's an established part of Ashton Lane. The fact it is a Belgian bar in the west end is often a footnote. The food menu has a particular Bruxelles vibe: steak frites, moules frites, poisson frites – you can see where they are going with this. Continue the continental tastes by dipping into melted French raclette cheese, served on a customer-operated hot plate, with venison sausage, chorizo, Parma ham and baby potatoes.

226 GALLOWGATE
226 Gallowgate, G4 0TS / 0141 564 1315 / 226gallowgate.com

The building has been here a long time. A staircase to nowhere, remnants of a tenemental past, is made into a feature above a rack of spirits behind the bar. Old walls are now uncovered and adorned sparingly with local art. Boiled gammon and buttered cabbage, grilled chicken and roast potatoes, bar snacks of salt beef fritters and goats cheese croquettes, beer battered haddock and weekend brunch options. They've recently opened a backyard garden area. A bar with no name, that's reimagining its place in the city.

THE DRAKE
1 Lynedoch St, G3 6EF
0141 332 7363
thedrakebar.co.uk

Confident cooking in a dog-friendly, comfy, old-fashioned bar. A hint of the countryside with Harris Tweed covered seating, a coal fire and front garden. The beef burger comes with caramelised onion, cheddar cheese and hand cut chips. Haggis bhajji and falafel for starters. Selection of Sunday roasts. Resident DJs playing until 1am at weekends.

THE SPARKLE HORSE
16 Dowanhill Street, G11 5QS
0141 562 3175
thesparklehorse.com

A firm favourite with the community and headquarters for local musicians since opening in December 2012. Good value main courses. Sweet potato and bean chilli is among the popular vegan options. St Mungo on tap and 14 different wines available.

BIER HALLE
9 Gordon Street, G1 3PL
0141 204 0706
republicbierhalle.com

Tucked away downstairs on Gordon Street, Bier Halle remains an important part of the food and drink scene in the city centre after 20 years of Staropramen pints and pizza. Beers from over 30 different countries. In good weather, they take over the street with outside dining just off Buchanan Street.

TABAC
10 Mitchell Lane, G1 3NU
0141 572 1448
tabacbar.com

A world of influences coalesce in this classy drinking den on Mitchell Lane. Take a break from the bustle of the city centre, grab the table by the window for a spot of people-watching. Brie, apple and radish salad, croque monsieur, fish with potato dauphinoise, or whatever goes best with your cocktail of choice.

THE FLYING DUCK

142 Renfield Street, G2 3AU

0141 564 1450 / theflyingduck.org

A basement bar, underground music venue and vegan diner in the city centre. A surprising, at times odd, soul food inspired menu, healthy drinks selection, pool table, gigs, clubs, quizzes, film screenings, drag karaoke and what can only be described as vibrant decor.

BAR BLOC+

117 Bath Street, G2 2SZ

bloc.ru

0141 574 6066 / bloc.ru

A forward-thinking, independent live music bar on Bath Street serving up a daily helping of satisfying food. Currently with a pop-up at 10 Claremont Street. Daily deals are popular with students and local office workers including Pasta Monday, Burger Tuesday and Steak Wednesday, all washed down with Scottish, German and American beers.

THE VARIETY BAR

401 Sauchiehall St, G2 3LG

0141 332 4449 / variety-bar.com

The slightly fusty vibe of a low-lit Art Deco bar, enlivened by DJs who work through funk, alternative, hip-hop, indie or techno, depending on the night. For drinks: Erdinger, Furstenburg, and Budvar, with craft beer options from Beavertown and Williams Bros. Pop in for cheese toasties made with sourdough bread, served until 5pm daily.

BAR SOBA

79 Albion Street, G1 1NY

barsoba.co.uk

0141 237 1551

Street food inspired by the night markets of South-East Asia, cocktails with a modern remix and the best of local DJs supplying the beats. Also on Byres Road and Mitchell Lane. Small plates, hot wok options and lots of dark rum, tequila and sake in the drinks at weekends.

BEST COCKTAILS
Mix it Up in the City

THE GATE
251 Gallowgate, G4 0TP / thegateglasgow.com

Look for the dramatic yellow flash on the outside of building and you will have found The Gate. A modern Scottish pub, it opened in the East End directly across from Barrowland Ballroom during summer 2019. Created by Andy Gemmell, after a career working in award-winning bars and travelling the world as a whisky ambassador.

As you step inside The Gate, the interior detail has been inspired by his love of traditional bars and travels to some of the worlds' best cocktail venues. Many original features have been retained including oak beams and the tenement close, through which you enter the bar. There's a nod to the Barras Market and its traders with framed pictures from Glasgow photographer Mark Leslie on the walls.

Drinks here have a big focus on Scottish brands with over 160 whiskies, alongside an expanding selection of 30 gins as well as craft beers, rums and liqueurs. Cocktails have been created by The Gate bartenders with a focus on simple and delicious ingredients,. A selection of six are updated every month by their team. Look for exciting takeovers by leading bars and bartenders. Try the cheese toastie with pecorino, gouda, spicy 'nduja and smoky paprika ketchup dip.

Order at the Bar: **The Jungle Boy – Plantation Pineapple Rum, Wray & Nephew Rum, Campari, citrus cordial, salt (£7.50)**

BEST COCKTAILS

THE IVY GLASGOW

106 Buchanan Street, G1 2NB / 01413781200 / theivyglasgow.com

Striking, stylish interiors, all-encompassing menus and friendly service from
sunrise to late in the evening. As well as the main restaurant, The Ivy features
two beautiful onyx bars and a glamorous private dining room, seating 24
guests. DJs and musicians provide regular entertainment on Thursday, Friday
and Saturday evenings for those dining upstairs or enjoying cocktails at the
first floor bar with views out over Buchanan Street.

Order at the Bar: **Chocolate Orange Negroni – Sipsmith Orange & Cacao
Gin, Campari, Belsazar Vermouth and chocolate bitters. (£9.75)**

GIN71

No.4 Virginia Court, G1 1TN / 0141 553 2326 / gin71.com

Gin71 opened in 2014, establishing their signature table service and a
revenance for the broad range of gins that form the core of the drinks menu.

Order at the Bar: **Blueberry Collins – Brockmans Gin,
Gin Bothy Blueberry, lemon juice, sugar and lemon tonic**

BEST COCKTAILS

WHEESHT

Claremont Street, G3 7HA

Glasgow's modern speakeasy, dreamed up by mixologist duo Jamie Moran and Dave Salvadord Ali, has a taste for the theatrical and a razor-sharp focus on the quality of the drinks they prepare. They've maintained an element of mystery about the location of the bar and willing customers arrive on a street corner close to Argyle Street to proffer a password in hope of gaining access. After the big reveal, you can simply order a favourite cocktail, take some suggestions from the bar or work to create a new sensation by freestyling on what should go in your drink. It's a performance piece with a rewarding conclusion.

THE CRESCENT

1102 Argyle Street, G3 7RX / crescentbar.co.uk

Good spirits and food to share. This corner of Finnieston is bathed in sunshine, when such a thing is available locally. Seats outside are prized. Inside it's plush seats, dark wood, stone walls, lots of space. The kind of bar you wouldn't mind losing a couple of hours. Weekend brunch comes with it's own cocktail menu featuring passionfruit punch, mimosas, Bloody Marys and breakfast martinis.

TIKI BAR & KITSCH INN

214 Bath St, G2 4HW / 0141 332 1341 / tikibarglasgow.com

No pretensions or artifice. Just strong drinks and a style that sits somewhere between outlandish and ridiculous. We like it. Say aloha to a basement bar with big personality, take a seat on a peacock chair and sip on a tropical cocktail served in a ceramic Tiki Mug. What else would you be doing on a Monday night? A splendid selection of rum, beer and snacks alongside a glittery, disco-tinged soundtrack. Thai food upstairs in the Kitsch Inn.

Order at the Bar: **Zombie – blend of five oak aged rums, apricot brandy, falernum, grenadine, cinnamon, absinthe and pink grapefruit, pineapple, lime juices (£11).**

THE SPIRITUALIST

62 Miller Street, G1 1DT / 0141 248 4165 / thespiritualistglasgow.com

Small groups huddle around glasses, many of them taking pictures, others staring in anticipation as ice cubes are cracked, dry ice is applied or extra elements are combined at your table. The presentation of your drinks at The Spiritualist will make you smile. Quirky names, clever combinations, customised glassware and the full gamut of crisp, sweet, sour and well balanced combinations. The largest bar gantry in the city, so chances are they will have the spirit you are looking for.

Order at the Bar: **Rhubarbra Streisand – Absolut Vanilia vodka, Edinburgh Gin Rhubarb and Ginger Liqueur, fresh lemon juice, sugar syrup, topped with Irn Bru (£8.50)**

BEST OF THE WEST
Destination Dining Close to Glasgow

SUGAR BOAT
30 Colquhoun Square, G84 8AQ / sugarboat.co.uk

Sugar Boat on Colquhoun Square in Helensburgh is a charming bistro, bar and wine shop, opened by owner Will Smith in 2017. If you make the short journey on the train from Queen Street Station, you'll find a beautifully presented dining room and impressive dishes showcasing the best of local produce. It was recently named AA Restaurant of the Year in Scotland and holds Bib Gourmand status from the Michelin Guide. The Head Chef, Scott Smith, is originally from Oban and the connection to the land and sea of the west of Scotland is a thread that runs through the menu.

When he initially opened his restaurant, Will told us: "I've big dreams – I want the locals to take us on board but I want to pull in a wider audience from Bearsden, Balloch, Clydebank. Use it as an excuse to come visit us here, take a walk along the front in Helensburgh, sit in the square."

On our last visit, we enjoyed the Isle of Mull cheddar farinette starter with olive and harissa. For mains, we chose a deep fish pie to delve into for a traditional lunch option by the Clyde.

CAMERON HOUSE AT LOCH LOMOND

Loch Lomond, Alexandria, G83 8QZ / 01389 310777 / cameronhouse.co.uk

It takes less than an hour to drive from the centre of Glasgow, follow the River Clyde, turn north and find yourself at the tranquil shore of one of Scotland's most impressive landscapes. They are nearing the conclusion of a careful restoration project that will see Cameron House Hotel, the leisure club, the Great Scots bar and Cameron Grill reopen in Spring 2020. The Cameron Spa, The Carrick Golf Course, The Marina, Cameron Lodges, The Boat House and Clubhouse remain open to visitors. We enjoy dinner at The Boat House with tranquil views over the marina. They serve fresh, local seafood dishes and stone-baked pizzas from a wood-burning oven. Arrive just before dusk to see the colours of the loch change as nightfall approaches.

MONADH KITCHEN

19 New Kirk Rd, G61 3SJ / 0141 258 6420 / monadhkitchen.co.uk

Sitting just outside Glasgow, Monadh Kitchen is a sophisticated Bearsden bistro that was set up by Martin Thliveros - you may remember him from his time at One Devonshire Gardens - and his wife Sharlene Harvey. Martin is Head Chef and Sharlene is your host as Restaurant Manager. Powerful Scottish flavours abound with cured Shetland mackerel, wild mountain hare, Tarbet crab, Isle of Barra monkfish and St Andrews cheddar featuring across the seasonally evolving menus. Bib Gourmand rated by Michelin since shortly after they opened in 2017 and widely celebrated as a benchmark of local quality. They prepare a Thursday Tasting Menu for a chance to take a tour of the best of Scottish produce amidst peaceful suburban surroundings.

AN INTRODUCTION TO THE CONTRIBUTORS

Paul Trainer grew up in East Kilbride, went to Strathclyde University, lived in the Merchant City, then spent 12 years working in local magazine and book publishing in Dublin and other places. He returned home to write at Glasgowist.com, a website celebrating the best people and places in the city. Last year, he wrote the Glasgow and West Coast Cook Book.

David Kirkwood is a freelance journalist based in the East End. He's been writing about food and drink in the city for more than a decade, with a particular interest in the bar and craft beer scenes. David is also a professional actor.

Rosalind Erskine is a magazine editor and journalist, covering interiors, travel, food and drink. She has worked for Harper's Bazaar and Time, living in London and Dubai. She now calls the West End home.

Clair Irwin studied Fine Art Photography at the Glasgow School of Art and has 20 years experience in the hospitality industry. A food and drink photographer and stylist, she has recently worked on film and television production for the BBC and HBO.

Sonya Walos is a Canadian photographer, cook, hospitality consultant and television presenter who lives and works in Glasgow city centre. She charts her culinary travels on Instagram at @worldofhungerlust.

Thanks are also due to: Oli Breidfjord and David Craik at Bright Signals. David Ward, Ian Corcoran, and Susan Sullivan at The Herald. Nicola Muir and Becky White at Atomic10.

Thank you to my family and friends for taking me to lunch.

RESTAURANT INDEX

GLASGOW'S BEST MENU

Within the 100 Best, you will see the best dishes to order at each of the restaurants included. Here, Glasgowist's editor, Paul Trainer, picks his favourite dishes of the past year.

STARTER

Barra Scallops,
Pancetta, Pea Purée
and a Pea & Shallot
Salad
(A'Challtainn)

MAIN COURSE

Abanico Iberico de
Bellota, Ratte Potato,
Hazelnut, Black Truffle
and Capers
(The Spanish Butcher)

DESSERT

Salted Caramel
Foundant,
Tonka Bean Ice Cream
(The Gannet)